INDIANS

BLACK HAWK, *Cleven*
OSCEOLA, *Clark*
POCAHONTAS, *Seymour*
PONTIAC, *Peckham*
SACAGAWEA, *Seymour*
SEQUOYAH, *Snow*
SITTING BULL, *Stevenson*
SQUANTO, *Stevenson*
TECUMSEH, *Stevenson*

NAVAL HEROES

DAVID FARRAGUT, *Long*
GEORGE DEWEY, *Long*
JOHN PAUL JONES, *Snow*
MATTHEW CALBRAITH PERRY, *Scharbach*
OLIVER HAZARD PERRY, *Long*
RAPHAEL SEMMES, *Snow*
STEPHEN DECATUR, *Smith*

NOTED WIVES
and MOTHERS

ABIGAIL ADAMS, *Wagoner*
DOLLY MADISON, *Monsell*
ELEANOR ROOSEVELT, *Weil*
JESSIE FREMONT, *Wagoner*
MARTHA WASHINGTON, *Wagoner*
MARY TODD LINCOLN, *Wilkie*
NANCY HANKS, *Stevenson*
RACHEL JACKSON, *Govan*

SCIENTISTS
and INVENTORS

ABNER DOUBLEDAY, *Dunham*
ALBERT EINSTEIN, *Hammontree*
ALECK BELL, *Widdemer*
CYRUS McCORMICK, *Dobler*
ELI WHITNEY, *Snow*
ELIAS HOWE, *Corcoran*
ELIZABETH BLACKWELL, *Henry*
GAIL BORDEN, *Paradis*
GEORGE CARVER, *Stevenson*
GEORGE EASTMAN, *Henry*
GEORGE PULLMAN, *Myers*
GEORGE WESTINGHOUSE, *Dunham*
HENRY FORD, *Aird and Ruddiman*
JOHN AUDUBON, *Mason*
JOHN BURROUGHS, *Frisbee*
JOHN DEERE, *Bare*
JOHN FITCH, *Stevenson*
LEE DeFOREST, *Dobler*
LUTHER BURBANK, *Burt*
MARIA MITCHELL, *Melin*
ROBERT FULTON, *Henry*
ROBERT GODDARD, *Moore*

SAMUEL MORSE, *Snow*
TOM EDISON, *Guthridge*
WALTER REED, *Higgins*
WILBUR AND ORVILLE WRIGHT, *Stevenson*

...RTON, *Stevenson*
DAN BEARD, *Mason*
DOROTHEA DIX, *Melin*
FRANCES WILLARD, *Mason*
J. STERLING MORTON, *Moore*
JANE ADDAMS, *Wagoner*
JOHN PETER ZENGER, *Long*
JULIA WARD HOWE, *Wagoner*
JULIETTE LOW, *Higgins*
LILIUOKALANI, *Newman*
LUCRETIA MOTT, *Burnett*
MOLLY PITCHER, *Stevenson*
OLIVER WENDELL HOLMES, JR., *Dunham*
SUSAN ANTHONY, *Monsell*

SOLDIERS

ANTHONY WAYNE, *Stevenson*
BEDFORD FORREST, *Parks*
DAN MORGAN, *Bryant*
DOUGLAS MACARTHUR, *Long*
ETHAN ALLEN, *Winders*
FRANCIS MARION, *Steele*
GEORGE CUSTER, *Stevenson*
ISRAEL PUTNAM, *Stevenson*
JEB STUART, *Winders*
NATHANAEL GREENE, *Peckham*
ROBERT E. LEE, *Monsell*
SAM HOUSTON, *Stevenson*
TOM JACKSON, *Monsell*
U. S. GRANT, *Stevenson*
WILLIAM HENRY HARRISON, *Peckham*
ZACK TAYLOR, *Wilkie*

STATESMEN

ABE LINCOLN, *Stevenson*
ANDY JACKSON, *Stevenson*
DAN WEBSTER, *Smith*
FRANKLIN ROOSEVELT, *Weil*
HENRY CLAY, *Monsell*
HERBERT HOOVER, *Comfort*
JAMES MONROE, *Widdemer*
JEFF DAVIS, *de Grummond and Delaune*
JOHN F. KENNEDY, *Frisbee*
JOHN MARSHALL, *Monsell*
TEDDY ROOSEVELT, *Parks*
WOODROW WILSON, *Monsell*

Walter Reed

Boy Who Wanted to Know

Illustrated by Al Fiorentino

Walter Reed

Boy Who Wanted to Know

by Helen Boyd Higgins

THE **BOBBS-MERRILL** COMPANY, INC.
A SUBSIDIARY OF HOWARD W. SAMS & CO., INC.
Publishers • INDIANAPOLIS • NEW YORK

For
Bruce Carmichael Higgins

Illustrations

Full pages

                                                         PAGE

Wat dived into the river.	25
Wat gulped the rest of his lemonade.	43
"All right now, you come off!"	50
"Pa always plants a tree before we move."	66
"Something might scare them back!"	90
"Take it back, take it back—"	124
In a little while Jim opened his eyes.	136
"I'm fine now," Evan said a while later.	156
He often rode miles to answer sick calls.	173
Reed hunted the cause of yellow fever.	189

Numerous smaller illustrations

Contents

	PAGE		PAGE
April Fool's Day	11	Young Reed	96
Doctor's Helpers	32	The Friday Exercises	111
The Big Wheel	55	Wat Takes Over	131
Evan's Secret	68	Wat Looks Ahead	145
On Their Way to Liberty	81	Dr. Walter Reed	162
		The Kill	177

Books by Helen Boyd Higgins

ALEC HAMILTON: THE LITTLE LION
JULIETTE LOW: GIRL SCOUT
STEPHEN FOSTER: BOY MINSTREL
WALTER REED: BOY WHO WANTED TO KNOW

Walter Reed

Boy Who Wanted to Know

April Fool's Day

It was a warm spring afternoon in 1859. Spring had come early that year to the pleasant little town of Farmville, Virginia. Along Main Street the tall chestnut trees were already in bloom.

One red brick house on Main Street was the Methodist parsonage. In its side yard grew a tall white oak tree. This afternoon a young cardinal whistled gaily from the very top of the tree.

Inside the parsonage seven-year-old Walter Reed whistled, too. He was going fishing with his best friend, Evan Macbeth, and his brother Christopher.

He was in the back hall, checking over the

things he would need. It always took Walter longer than the other boys to get ready. He liked to make careful preparations. Now he sat down on the floor, cross-legged, to test his stubby hickory fishing pole. He made sure the line was fastened carefully to the end.

He picked up a top-shaped bobber and turned it about slowly. He was very proud of it. It was the first one he had whittled all by himself.

For a moment he stopped whistling. "You're a beauty," he said aloud. "My initials show up mighty nice on your side. I got the letters even."

He began to whistle again, softly. He tied his fishline around a groove near the top of the bobber. Then he pulled it down tight and wedged it into a deep slot near the bottom. He jerked the line several times to make sure his knots would hold.

"Hey, Wat! What's keeping you? We can't wait all afternoon," Evan shouted from next door. He was eight years old and had red hair and freckles.

"Come on, Wat!" called his ten-year-old brother, Kit.

"In just a minute, Kit. I have to get my worms," Wat shouted back through the open window in the hall.

He jumped to his feet. From the pocket of his worn blue knee pants he pulled a small chunk of basswood. The point of his fishhook was pushed deep into the soft wood, to keep it safe. He put the basswood back in his pocket.

"Fishing pole, line, bobber, hook. Now my worms," he muttered. He hitched his red suspenders up over the shoulders of his patched shirt. "Coming!" he called.

His sister, Laura, who was sixteen and usually acted very grown-up, heard him. She and Ma were in the sitting room, sewing.

"Now's my chance to fool Wat," Laura whispered. Her brown eyes danced. "He'll be sure to come in to tell you he's going out. Wat never forgets that."

Ma nodded and smiled. Laura and her mother were very much alike. They were both pretty and quick in their movements. They both loved a good joke.

A moment later Wat stuck his head into the sitting room. "I'm going fishing with Kit and Evan, Ma. We might get a whole bucket of sunnies for supper."

"Why, Walter Reed, what's that all over your hair? It looks like—like whitewash!" Laura said in a surprised tone. "Look in the mirror!"

Wat came into the room. He pushed a stool under the mirror, climbed up on it, and peered into the glass. His straw-colored hair was mussed up, as usual, but that was all.

"April fool! April fool!" his sister teased.

Now Wat understood. This was one of Laura's

14

jokes! Today was the right day for jokes and tricks, too. "Aw, I forgot this is the first day of April." His face was red and he looked so sheepish that even his mother laughed with Laura. "Did you fool Kit, too?"

"No," said Ma, patting his shoulder. "You can have that fun."

"I'll fool Evan, too. It may make him mad," Wat said with a grin, "but he'll get over it."

He walked slowly to the back door. What could he do to fool the boys? He could see Evan and Kit, waiting on the Macbeths' porch. They weren't looking in his direction.

Then Wat saw Miss Lucy, who kept a little shop, come by. She waved to Kit and Evan. Whenever he saw her, Wat thought of the peppermint candy she sold. Then he usually thought of how much it cost. Today this gave him another idea.

His blue eyes sparkled. "I know, I know!" he said to himself. He grabbed up his bait box and ran next door.

"Well, it's about time you came," Evan said with a frown.

"I'm sorry. I had to—uh, do an errand for Ma down to Miss Lucy's," Wat said slowly. "You'll never guess what happened on the way."

16

"What?" asked the other boys together.

"I found twenty-five cents, a whole *quarter*, right on the sidewalk. So I picked it up and——"

"You couldn't have found that much!" Kit interrupted quickly.

"Let's see it," Evan demanded.

"I can't show it to you. I don't have it. I spent every cent of it for peppermint candy."

"Twenty-five cents for candy!" Kit exclaimed. "Oh, Wat, what will Pa say? Didn't you save a tenth of it for the collection in Sunday school?"

"Didn't you bring us any candy?" Evan asked. "You couldn't eat that much by yourself."

"I could, but I didn't," Wat said truthfully. "Look in my pockets. Help yourselves."

Kit and Evan dug in, one on each side. The pockets were empty. Wat shouted, "April fool!"

For just a moment both boys were too surprised to move. This moment gave Wat a chance to sprint across the back field. Even

17

though the stubble hurt his bare feet he didn't stop until he was on the other side of the fence. Then he waited for the boys.

"Think you're funny, don't you? Well, I don't," Evan grumbled. "Just you wait. I'll get even with you, Wat Reed!"

Kit laughed. "*I* think it's funny—and so would you, Evan, if you had thought it up. Just the same I'll get back at you, too, Wat, and I'll make it a good trick!"

WAT'S WHALE

Evan was still frowning as they picked their way carefully along a stony path. It led down to the shore of the slow-moving Appomattox River. A rickety old wharf jutted out into the water. The boys' favorite fishing hole was just off the end of the wharf.

Kit and Evan filled the fish buckets with fresh

water, ready to hold their catch. They baited
their hooks, but had to wait for Wat to test again
the knot that held his bobber.

"Ready, slowpoke?" Evan asked.

"Ready," said Wat at last. "Spit!"

They spat on their worms, closed their eyes,
and tossed their lines in at the same moment.
They were sure this would bring them luck.

When they opened their eyes, the three boys
grinned at one another. "Well, I guess I'll catch
a twenty-pound bass," Evan announced.

"You will?" Kit challenged. "Then I'll pull
in a man-eating shark. It'll gobble up your little
old bass!"

Wat laughed. "I'll catch me a whale! He'll
snap up your bass and your shark, like that."
Wat snapped his fingers.

The boys settled down to wait for a nibble.
The three homemade bobbers tipped gently with
the small waves. It was good to be down by the

river today. The sun was warm, but there was a cool breeze. It was still too early for the mosquitoes that bothered fishermen in the summer.

The boys watched a belted kingfisher swoop down to the weedy water near by. The beautiful bird soared up again with a small, wriggling fish in its beak.

This afternoon the sunfish, which were about all the younger boys of Farmville ever caught, were biting well. The buckets were soon half full. Wat held one fish in his hand for a minute and examined it closely before he tossed it in with the others.

"I wonder why each sunny looks different," he said slowly as he baited his hook again. "All sunnies have the same number of yellow, blue, and red stripes. But the stripes aren't always in the same places."

Evan said, "We've caught about enough now. Let's quit and go home."

"No, we'll need more," Kit objected. "Pa may be home for supper. He's been away at Conference, to find out about his new circuit."

The Reverend Lemuel Sutton Reed was a minister of the Methodist Church. He had to be away from home a great deal, for he was a circuit rider. He held services for all the Methodist congregations in the county around Farmville. He went from one to another, riding his horse, Queenie, miles and miles over the rough roads in all kinds of weather, winter and summer. Every two years his bishop assigned him to a new circuit, in another place.

"You won't move away from Farmville soon, will you?" asked Evan.

"Oh, yes, we'll probably go this fall," Wat answered. "It's fun to travel. We see new places and meet new people. It's grand to have Pa a circuit rider."

"Wat likes it, but the rest of us don't. No

sooner do we make friends than we have to leave them," said Kit.

"We make more friends all the time, don't we, Kit?" Wat argued. "When we lived in Murfreesboro, in North Carolina, we didn't know we were going to like it here in Farmville so much, did we? And when we——"

"Wat, your bobber! It's gone clear under," Evan said suddenly. "You must have a big one on your hook."

"Oh, April fool!" Wat had been expecting Evan to try some trick.

"No, it's not," Kit said seriously. "Look out or it'll pull your pole out of your hands!"

Wat had already felt the strong tug on his line. He scrambled to his feet, holding tight to his pole. "I've got my whale!" he shouted.

Down in the river a fish broke water.

"It's a catfish!" Wat yelled. "I saw the spots. Did you see it?"

Kit ordered sharply, "Calm down. You know a 'cat' always fights to get the hook out of its mouth. Be careful now! Don't let your line go slack. Want me to help?"

Wat shook his head. "No! I can land it." He braced himself for the struggle.

Now his line was taut. The pole was pulled from side to side as the fish zigzagged for its life. Suddenly the fish stopped fighting and disappeared under the surface.

"Oh, now your line's slack," Evan said excitedly. "That's just what the fish wants!"

In a few moments the line was taut again, and was stretched almost straight down from the end of the wharf.

"Watch out now!" Kit said. "Steady. You're doing fine. But your cat's hiding in the weeds under the wharf."

Wat didn't answer for a moment. He was too busy. There was so much pull on his line that his pole was bending. "The cat's—not giving up——" He gasped. "Help, Kit! My pole is breaking!" There was a sound of splintering wood. All that he was left holding was a sliver of rod. "Grab the line! Don't let it get away. Help, Evan! Quick!"

Kit threw himself on the line just in time. Evan grabbed the short piece of pole that was attached. In another second Wat had it firmly in his hands.

"Now your line's fraying. It's going to break, too! It's rubbing on the edge of a broken board," Evan warned. "Wat, *look out!*"

His warning came too late. The catfish was swimming out into deep water. Most of Wat's line was trailing behind it.

"You'll never land that fish," Evan remarked.

Wat's eyes flashed. His jaw was set. Before Kit or Evan could say another word, there was a splash. Wat had dived into the river. When he

came up to the surface, he gasped, "I'll bring—it in—by hand."

The boys saw that he was treading water, and they knew he was trying to catch sight of his line. Then they saw something else. The fish was swimming toward Wat! Suddenly it sensed danger and disappeared under the wharf.

"It's gone for sure this time," Evan shouted. "You did the best you could."

"Come on back, Wat. You can't do anything else about it," Kit called.

Wat was afraid they were right. He was so disappointed that he swam around and around, just hoping. Finally he started for the shore.

Then, not three feet from his hands, he saw a fishline trailing. Beneath the surface was a dark shadow. Wat caught the line and pulled it gently toward him.

The boys on the wharf were cheering and giving him plenty of advice.

"Maybe it's fooling and isn't tired at all," Kit shouted. "Look out for the spines on its fins!"

Wat knew that these spines were as sharp as knives. He waited for his chance. When the fish came to the surface he grabbed it behind the gills. Then, just kicking his feet, he headed toward the wharf. The boys took Wat's prize first. When they pulled Wat up, the big fish was flopping about on the dry boards.

After one look, Wat ran down the wharf toward the shore. He called over his shoulder, "I'll get a stone and hit it on the head to stop its suffering."

Evan turned to Kit. "Quick! You empty all of the sunnies into one bucket, and I'll put the catfish in the other. We can hide the bucket with the catfish in it behind that post. We'll make Wat think the catfish flopped back into the water. To April-fool him, you know."

When Wat came back the boys were lying at

the end of the wharf. They seemed to be looking at something down in the water.

"See another big one?" he asked. "I'll help you get it. Just let me take care of my fish first."

The boys glanced at each other as he cried in alarm, "Where *is* my fish?"

"It just flopped right back," Evan said.

"We're awfully sorry, Wat," Kit added.

"Why didn't you jump in after it?" Wat asked them angrily.

"In that cold water? Not me!" Kit said.

Evan laughed. "April fool! April fool! We caught you that time. Look in my fish bucket. It's behind that post."

Wat did. His back was toward the boys as he lifted up his fish. Then he whirled around. "I don't think that was a bit funny," he stormed.

"What if you had thought up the idea?" Evan asked with a smile.

"Well—yes, you're right. It was your turn

to fool me." Wat's teeth chattered as he added, "You were right about that water, too. It *was* cold! B-r-r!"

"Better take off that wet shirt," Kit said, "and we'd better go home."

CAT'S WHISKERS FOR LUCK

The boys went home by Main Street instead of crossing the back field again. It was a little farther, but their feet weren't used to the stubble yet. This was the first day they had gone barefoot. On the way they met Dr. Morris. Wat showed him the catfish.

"Couldn't have done better myself," said the kindly, white-haired doctor. "Your pa's home, Walter. He's going to be mighty proud of you."

Wat was happier than ever over this news. He and the other boys ran off to the parsonage.

When they came into the yard, they saw the

whole Reed family on the porch. Ma and Laura had brought their sewing out. Twelve-year-old Tom was balancing himself on the railing. Bessie Sue, the cook and family friend, had come out from the kitchen.

They were all listening to Pa tell about the Methodist Conference. Only Jim paid no attention. Long-legged Jim, who was fourteen, looked like his father, with his dark hair and eyes. Sometimes he laughed and joked like his mother. Usually, though, he had his nose buried in a book.

"Hello, Pa!" called Wat. "I just caught a great big catfish! I landed it myself. Tom, I want to know how much it weighs."

Tom was the best fisherman in the family. He was jolly and very strong, with broad shoulders. Now he jumped down from the railing and came to meet his little brother. He picked up the catfish expertly and balanced it from hand to hand.

"A good four pounds—maybe five. Jim, come see what you think."

All the Reed boys liked to fish. Jim put down his book, came over, and took Wat's catch. "Nearer four," he said honestly.

Pa admired it also. Ma and Laura said it was handsome, but they didn't look at it closely.

"What fine whiskers that cat has!" Jim said. "Wat, be sure to save those. You should fasten them to the end of your pole for luck."

Bessie Sue said, "I'm going to fry that big fish right now for supper. But I'll surely save those whiskers for you, Wat." She hurried off to the kitchen.

"Wat doesn't have a fishing pole left to fasten the whiskers on," said Kit.

"No pole! How in the world did you land it?" Pa said. "Tell us about it, son."

Wat grinned as the family sat down on the steps. Even Jim listened as Wat told the story.

Doctor's Helpers

WAT'S BROTHER helped him find a strong hickory stick. Wat made himself a new pole. He fastened the catfish whiskers carefully at the top of it. Tom gave him a brand new fishing line and two sharp, new hooks.

Then the weather turned rainy. For two months Wat had few chances to use his pole, but in June the fishing was good. Yet, hard as he wished and tried for another big fish, he caught only sunnies.

In July even the sunfish wouldn't bite. It was the hottest month Farmville had known for years. By the time August came, Wat had decided that even catfish whiskers attached to his pole brought him no good luck.

One afternoon Wat and Evan were out in the shady yard of the parsonage. All summer they had been together every waking hour. They always helped each other with chores, to get through faster. Now they couldn't decide how to spend their free time.

"I wish I had some work to do," Wat said suddenly. "Don't you, Evan?"

Evan looked at him in surprise. "We've done plenty today. We fed and watered the chickens. We collected eggs. We weeded flower beds and the vegetable garden and——"

"Oh, I don't mean chores. I mean a real pay job, like Tom's."

Tom Reed had been away all summer. He was working on one of the river barges that carried tobacco from the big tobacco market in Petersburg to a seaport on the coast.

"Tom's earned a lot of money," Wat went on. "I'd like to see Petersburg, too. It's bigger than any of the towns we've lived in."

"Why didn't Jim, too, get a job there?"

"Because he was going to study with Mr. Allen—you know, the one who used to be a teacher. Jim wants to get ahead of his class so he can go to college sooner."

Just then Kit came out and joined the boys. "Whew, it's hot!"

Kit pulled out his jackknife. "Want to play mumblety-peg?"

Usually Wat was good at this game. He knew all the knife tricks. Today, however, he didn't seem to pay attention.

"What's the matter with you?" Kit said at last. "It's your turn again."

"I was thinking about a new fishing pole."

At Kit's puzzled look Evan explained, "He means a pole we saw at Miss Lucy's shop."

34

Wat's eyes gleamed. "It's extra-long, but it costs a quarter."

"How much money do you have?" Evan wanted to know.

"Eighteen cents. Ma hasn't had any special chores lately. She's the only one who ever pays me for my work," Wat said in a discouraged tone of voice.

"Well, you need only seven cents more. Ask your pa for them," Evan said. "Couldn't you do that, Wat?"

Wat shook his head. "Pa never has any money for things like that. He sends all his spare cash to missionaries in foreign lands."

"Even if Pa would give Wat the money," Kit said, "he won't be home for a long time. He has to preach more in the summer. There are all-day meetings at all his churches then."

"Yes, I'll have to earn it somehow." Wat took the knife and flipped it off his elbow.

The next day Wat and Evan went down to Miss Lucy's shop. They often dropped in, to see if she needed any help. Sometimes she asked them to sweep out the shop. Sometimes there were new goods to unpack. Miss Lucy always gave the boys three peppermint balls apiece for such work.

Today Wat wanted to take another look at the unusual fishing pole.

It was much longer than his brothers' poles. It was slim and smooth. It looked like several sections of pale wood jointed together.

"That pole's made from a bamboo plant," Miss Lucy told the boys. "It came all the way from the Orient. The salesman told me about it. He said it's light but very strong. It's so limber it will bend without breaking."

Wat wanted to try bending it, to see how limber it was, but Miss Lucy wouldn't let him.

36

"The salesman might have been wrong," she said. "I won't take a chance. He talked me into buying one, and it was expensive. I must get at least a quarter for it."

"If I buy it—" Wat was thinking aloud— "maybe I could land another big fish. If it's limber, then it would bend enough to let a big fish run till it's tired."

"Have you that much money?" Miss Lucy asked quickly.

"Not yet, but I'll get it soon. Well, good-by, Miss Lucy."

She had no chores for them, so the boys went outside. They lay down on the grass, and put their straw hats over their faces to keep off mosquitoes. Neither spoke for a while.

All of a sudden Evan sat up. "Why don't you borrow from Jim? You said he has a lot of money hidden in an old sock."

"Reeds don't hold with borrowing," Wat an-

37

swered. "I might not be able to pay it back. Jim is saving to go to college."

Evan found this hard to understand. "That pole will probably be sold before you earn seven cents. I tell you what! I'll ask my pa for the money and give it to you, for keeps."

"No, it isn't my birthday or Christmas or anything. I couldn't take it," Wat said firmly. "Thanks just the same."

As Wat spoke, Dr. Morris drove up to his house across the road. "If it were spring, we might gather plants for Doctor Ed. He needs a lot to make his medicines. Sometimes he'll pay for them——"

Evan jumped to his feet. "I've got an idea! Maybe Doctor Ed needs some fresh ones. Let's ask him. Come on! He'll pay a penny apiece for them, I know."

Wat raised his hat to look at his friend. "A penny for an old plant?"

"No—for a fresh leech!" Evan was excited. "Come on, Wat! Doctor Ed just drove in."

"You mean those little black things like snails that get on us when we're wading?"

"No, they're just babies. They don't stick tight. I mean the soft, flat, big, queery-gray ones that look like worms."

Dr. Morris came out on his porch. "Howdy, boys." After one keen glance he added, "Not patients today, are you?"

They both shook their heads. "No, sir!"

"Well, I just finished my rounds. I'm going to have some nice, cool lemonade before my office hours begin. May I prescribe some lemonade for you?"

"Yes, sir!" They both nodded.

The doctor called to his cook, "Oh, Liza! Two more glasses of lemonade, please, and a few cookies." He sat down in a rocking chair. "Now, what are you up to on this hot day?"

"I want to make some money. I need it right away," Wat said.

"Most boys do." Doctor Ed chuckled. "What did you see at Miss Lucy's shop today that you would like to buy?"

Wat flushed, so Evan spoke up. "A fishing pole. It's made of bamboo, and it costs a quarter. It will bend, but it won't break."

"I'm not sure about that," Wat said seriously. "The salesman only told Miss Lucy that. I want to find out."

Liza brought out the tall glasses of lemonade and a whole plate of cookies she had just baked. They were delicious.

Dr. Morris sipped his lemonade. He rocked back and forth several times before he said, "A bamboo fishing pole, eh? What will they think of next! When I was a boy," he went on, "I made my own pole out of a good stout stick. It cost nothing but a little time."

40

Wat nodded. "I had one like that, but it broke. I'd like to try this new kind."

"So do you need any leeches, Doctor Ed?" Evan put in eagerly. "You said I found fine ones for you last summer. That was while you and Kit were down in North Carolina with your grandparents, Wat," he added.

"You out of money, too, young man?"

"No, Doctor—I'm just helping Wat. He needs seven cents."

The old man said, "Hmm. Well, I guess I could use a few leeches. The mosquitoes would eat you alive if you went down by the river today, though. Wait for a cool, windy day. Wind will blow the mosquitoes away."

"We don't know when it will be cool and windy. I don't mind mosquitoes—at least I don't mind them much," Wat said.

"We'll make sassafras bug-medicine," said Evan. "That'll help our bites."

Wat explained. "If we wait, the pole may be sold." He gulped the rest of his lemonade. "Exactly how many leeches do you need, Doctor Ed? I'll get them, if Evan will just show me how, and where to go. I'd like to know about them."

"You *are* determined." Dr. Morris chuckled again. "Well, I don't suppose a few extra mosquito bites will bother you youngsters. I could use about six leeches. You might get me some sassafras leaves, too. I'm just about out of bug-medicine myself."

He told Liza to bring a sack for the leaves, and his leech bucket. The boys hurried back to the parsonage, to get Wat's savings and to see if Kit would go with them.

"Where do you find leeches?" Wat asked.

"You find them in the river, under stones or logs," Evan told him. "They have a suction disk at both ends. They clamp on you with those disks, and then they bite you and suck out blood."

42

"How awful!" Kit said. "Why does Doctor Ed want any?"

"He puts them on sick people, to suck out some of their blood."

"Why does he do that?" Wat asked in a surprised voice. He hadn't stopped to wonder why Doctor Ed wanted leeches.

"Don't you know about bloodletting? Why, doctors nearly always take out some of your blood if you have a fever. They can cut your arm and let blood out, or they can put leeches on you. Doctor Ed put one on me, a long time ago, when I had a fever. He said it would suck out any bad blood, and this would help bring down my fever."

Kit said, "Ugh!"

"Did it help?" Wat asked.

"It must have, because I got well. I'd been awfully sick, too. That's the longest time I ever had a leech on me," Evan boasted. "Of course some got on my legs when I was little and used to go wading a lot. When you hunt them, they usually find you first." Evan giggled at the look on Kit's face. "You just pull them off."

Kit didn't like that idea, but he decided to come along anyhow.

SASSAFRAS AND LEECHES

Evan suggested, "Let's cut through the grove on the bluff above the river. We can get sassafras leaves there. Then we can make bug-medicine while we work."

"How do we make it?" Wat asked.

"Oh, you just chew up some leaves till they're like paste in your mouth. It tastes sort of spicy. Then you put that on your bug bites and it takes out the sting or itching."

"Is that the way Doctor Ed makes his bug-medicine?" asked Kit.

"Goodness, no!" Evan said. "His is to put on other people. He dries the leaves and powders them. Then he mixes the powder with lard and a little salt."

After the boys had filled their pockets with leaves, Evan led the way down to the shore. He headed toward a cove where willow trees leaned out over the muddy water. There were mossy rocks under them. Mosquitoes buzzed in clouds about the boys' heads.

Kit slapped at them. "We'd better make bug-medicine first!"

"No, let's get the leeches first," Wat said.

Evan agreed with Kit. So they chewed the sassafras leaves as fast as they could, and each boy plastered the paste on his bites.

"Now roll your pants legs up high," Evan ordered. "Wade in and start hunting."

"In that dirty water? I'll bet there's oozy mud on the bottom," Kit said.

"There is," Wat called. "It squishes up between my toes. What do I do first? Where are the leeches, Evan?"

"Under rocks or logs," Evan said. "The kind of leeches Doctor Ed wants are about half as long as my hand."

"Are there other kinds?"

"Yes, but they're no good for sick people. They're just babies. And there's another kind that only gets on fish or turtles. The kind Doctor Ed wants hunch themselves up into a blob. The others are always long. That's how you tell 'em apart. Come on in, Kit. It's not bad."

"No, I'm not going leeching," Kit said firmly. "I'll gather the sassafras leaves." He took the sack and went back to the grove.

It was hard to turn the heavy rocks. The mud underfoot was very slippery. Mosquitoes still buzzed and bit. One of Evan's eyelids was soon swollen with bites.

Wat said in a worried tone, "Evan, you just show me how to find one leech and then you go help Kit. These buzzers are awful. It isn't fair for you to suffer for my fishing pole."

"You want it, don't you? You're my best friend, aren't you? Well, don't be silly."

Wat felt happy in spite of the mosquitoes. "Of course you can use it part of the time," he said.

Evan didn't answer. He was staring at Wat's leg. "Hey, maybe we haven't found one, but two have certainly found you."

Wat glanced down and saw what looked like two blobs of mud on his right leg.

"Come out on the shore and I'll show you how to get them off."

They stepped out of the water. Evan took hold of one of the leeches around the middle and pulled. Its body stretched, but the ends stuck tight to Wat's leg. Evan yanked at it. The leech just stretched more.

48

Wat made a wry face. "Won't you pull the leech in two?" he asked.

"I never have yet. There!" The leech had suddenly let loose. Evan held it up. "See how fat he is? He's full of your blood."

The leech had pulled itself up into a roundish blob again. Evan dropped it into Doctor Ed's bucket of muddy water. He made sure the cover, which had some air holes in it, was on tight.

"You can take off your other one," he said.

Wat sat down on a rock and took a close look at his leg. He didn't notice that Kit was beside him until his brother said, "Do you need some more sassafras leaves?"

"Oh, Kit, look! I've caught two leeches!" Wat cried excitedly. "One's in the bucket. See where it bit me? There are three little cuts. Leeches must have three teeth."

At the sight of blood Kit's face turned pale. He ran back to the grove.

"I guess it made me feel kind of sick, too, when I first went leeching," Evan said kindly.

Wat admitted, "I felt funny in my stomach when you pulled that one off me, but leeching doesn't make me sick. It's interesting, and if the leeches will help Doctor Ed's patients——"

Now he bent over the queer-looking worm clamped on his leg. It had rings around it, like an angleworm, but it was much wider in the middle. Wat poked at one end. He could not move the leech. He pulled at the middle, and it stretched. He pulled harder and harder, but the leech only stretched like rubber.

"All right now, you come off! I'm going to give one long pull instead of little tugs, and see what happens."

It took a strong, steady pull before the leech finally let go. Wat stowed it away in the bucket and waded out into the mud for more.

Soon Evan found two under a log. After what

seemed a long time, Wat spotted two more on a rock. Both boys were tired now. They were so itchy, hot, and muddy that they went for a quick swim in the fresh water beyond the cove.

WAT GETS HIS POLE

When they climbed up the bluff they found Kit waiting. He had a sack full of sassafras leaves. They sat down to rest for a few minutes. Up here the mosquitoes weren't so bad.

"Leeching is a pretty hard way to make money," Kit remarked. "I'll never be a doctor. I'd hate to carry those slimy things around."

Wat said thoughtfully, "Doctors do lots of good for people. I might be one when I grow up, or maybe a minister——"

"Not me," said Kit. "I want to be a lawyer."

Evan said, "I'm going to grow tobacco and cotton. I'll have a great big plantation, but I'll live in Farmville. I'm going to have a pair of the finest horses in all Virginia, too!"

"I don't know where I'll live," Wat said. "Lots of places, I hope. Are you going to college, Evan?"

"No, I won't have to go to college to learn how to raise tobacco. Anyhow, I don't like school so much as you do."

"Pa says college is the best place to find out about everything. There are so many things I want to know."

"I wish you'd stay here in Farmville," Evan said. "We could be partners on my plantation."

"Well, I'll think about it. Come on, we'd better go. Somebody might buy my pole."

Dr. Morris was very pleased with the leeches. He gave Wat a penny for each leech, and he gave Kit three pennies for the leaves.

They hurried across the road to Miss Lucy's. Kit admired the bamboo pole, and thought it was worth a quarter. "Here, Wat, you take my money," he said. "I didn't really work for it. Besides, Evan and I came along to help you."

"But you gathered all the leaves for Doctor Ed," Wat argued. "You ought to keep two cents for that. I need only one more penny, anyway."

Then he bought the pole. The minute Miss Lucy had the money in her hand, Wat bent the tip of his new property. He did it again, and again, a little farther each time.

"Wow! It springs right back!" he said happily. "Look, Miss Lucy! That salesman was right. You've seen me test it. Now you know for sure it doesn't break."

Then Kit bought two cents' worth of peppermint balls for them to eat, in honor of Wat's new fishing pole.

The Big Wheel

THE BOYS all agreed that the long bamboo pole
made an improvement in fishing. Now Wat
was able to drop his bait out into deeper water.
The sunnies he caught were bigger than the
fish Kit and Evan landed. But all three of the
boys knew there was little chance of getting
another really big fish this late in the summer.

Wat didn't care much, for he had something
more important on his mind. Pa had asked him
to take care of Queenie for two whole weeks. Pa
had to go over to Richmond for the District
Conference. Pa couldn't ride Queenie, because
he would stay in the city and would wear his

best clothes every day. He planned to travel in a public coach to this important meeting.

Wat was delighted. Evan helped him with Queenie. For the first time in their lives, he and Evan had a horse of their own!

Tom was still away, on his last river trip before school started. Kit had gone to North Carolina to visit Grandpa and Grandma White. Jim was studying harder than ever, getting ready for examinations. Wat and Evan didn't have to share Queenie with anyone.

The boys had taken turns in all the work of caring for her. They had had lots of fun, too. They had exercised the mare by riding double for miles around the countryside.

One morning early in September both boys were out in the barn. Wat was whistling as he groomed Queenie. He had to stand on a wooden box to reach the top of her neck with the curry-comb. Evan was cleaning out Queenie's stall near by. The minister would return today, so both horse and stall had to be especially clean.

As Wat began to brush Queenie's mane he called, "I'm just sure those tracks we saw in the S.H.P. weren't your dog's. They were smaller than Blackie's would be. Besides, a dog walks on its toes. This animal put its feet down flat. It must have, because the sole part of its track was deeper than the toes."

The S.H.P. was Wat and Evan's Secret Hiding Place. Wat had found it long ago when he was chasing a hen. No one else knew about it except Kit. It was a hollow that ran far back under the high floor of the Reeds' barn. Its entrance was overgrown with tall weeds. Yesterday when the boys had crawled into it they had discovered the strange tracks.

At last Evan came out of Queenie's stall. He hung up the pitchfork and rubbed his hand on his pants. "I didn't notice. They looked like

Blackie's prints to me. Why do you always have to examine every single little detail? What difference does it make whose tracks they were?" He went to get some fresh straw for the stall.

"Only that I want to know what sort of animal was in there," Wat called. "I'm going to find out what it was, too."

"Well, don't expect me to help you with that," Evan said rather crossly, as he scattered straw on the floor.

Wat stared down at him. Evan had been very touchy for the last few days. "Have you got a headache again?"

"No, it stopped yesterday afternoon. I just feel tired. Are you sure your pa is coming today?"

Wat nodded. "I'm sort of sorry he is, because we'll not have Queenie to ride any more. Still, I do want to know when we're going to move and where we're going."

"Well, I guess I'll go home for breakfast.

Come over and tell me as soon as you find out about moving."

"I will," Wat promised, and Evan walked slowly toward the Macbeth house. Wat wondered whether his friend was sick. "Maybe he's just unhappy because I'm moving away," Wat decided at last. "There, Queenie, you look wonderful. Pa will be proud of you."

Just then he heard a buggy drive up in front of the parsonage, and the sound of voices. "That must be Pa!" Wat let Queenie into her stall, closed the door, and raced around to the front.

The buggy was driving away, but there was Pa on the porch, with Ma.

"Hello!" Wat called. "Wait till you see Queenie! How did you get here so early?"

"We drove most of the night," Pa answered with a smile.

"He rode home with another minister who's going on to Lynchburg," Ma explained.

"Well, where will we move? When do we go? Could I ride Queenie part of the way? Could I, Pa? Please?"

Pa laughed and tousled Wat's hair. "Pharaba, the boy is still wound up!"

Ma laughed, too, and Laura and Jim came to the door to see what the commotion was. They were delighted to find Pa.

Bessie Sue claimed she wasn't a bit surprised. She'd had a feeling in her bones he'd be home in time for breakfast.

By the time Ma had asked about the Bishop's health and Pa had told her about the friends he'd seen, Bessie Sue had her best battercakes ready. Pa said he would answer no more questions till he had eaten this fine breakfast.

The moment Pa laid down his fork Wat begged, "Now, please tell us."

Pa pulled a hand-drawn map from his pocket. When the family was about to move, the Bishop always gave one to Pa. It was more useful to the Reeds than a printed map of the state, for it showed the houses where they would stay each night along the way. It also showed, by many small dots, all of Pa's new charges. These were the small churches to which he would travel on his circuit.

Pa pointed to a big red dot on the map, almost straight west of Farmville. "This is our new home—the town of Liberty, in Bedford County. It's about sixty miles from here, in the foothills of the Blue Ridge Mountains."

Wat exclaimed, "Why, Pa, we'll get to live near the mountains for the first time!"

"I'm pleased about that," Pa said. "I understand the climate is more healthful than it is in the Tidewater towns where we've been. Mountain air is purer. There in the hills, we'll have none of the miasmas, or poisonous vapors, that rise from low, swampy ground."

Ma asked, "When do you plan to leave, Lemuel? How long will it take us to get there?"

"I'd like to leave just as soon as you can get ready, Pharaba. The minister who had the Bedford circuit has already gone on to his new one. So the people there need me now. Could we be on our way a week from today?"

"A week!" Wat echoed. "Oh, Pa, that would be September thirteenth—my birthday. We couldn't leave then."

"I'm afraid we can't help it this year, son. Isn't God's work more important than your birthday?" Wat blushed, and Pa went on. "It will take us at least ten days to reach Liberty. I'll have to spend a couple of days at some of the places along the way."

"Please, may I go tell Evan now?" At his mother's nod Wat leaped up and rushed out. His family could hear him jump down the porch steps two at a time.

His mother smiled. "Wat's excited over the move," she said.

"He's not old enough yet to care as much about his friends as the rest of us do," Laura said. "When he's been away a few days, he'll probably forget all about Evan."

"That's not quite fair, Laura," Ma said quickly. "I understand exactly how he feels. Both of us want to see what's around the next corner, or in the next town."

"As for forgetting friends, I doubt it. Wat's like his mother," Pa said, smiling at Ma. "She's still devoted to the friends we made in every town we've lived in."

"Well, I can't help feeling bad about leaving. I'll miss the Farmville girls terribly."

In the meantime Wat had rushed over to the Macbeths'. His friend was sitting on the porch. "Evan! We're going to move on my birthday!"

"Oh, no!" Evan exclaimed. "Where?"

"To Liberty. That's a town in Bedford County—near the Blue Ridge Mountains," Wat said. Then he added, "Will you come and visit me next summer?"

"Wat, that would be great! Did you ask your parents about it?"

"Not yet, but I'm sure it'll be all right with them. Let's go back now and I'll show you Pa's new circuit."

When the two boys came back into the parsonage dining room, the map was still spread on the table. Wat pointed out Liberty. "Pa, let's show Evan where your new circuit is. You know, the wheel that you've shown us."

His father smiled and pulled a pencil from his pocket. Wat took it and drew a line connecting all the dots that surrounded Liberty. "There's the rim of the wheel. That's the boundary of the circuit, and Liberty is the hub of the wheel. Now, Pa, you put in the spokes."

Pa took the pencil. Carefully he drew a line from the hub out to each dot on the rim.

"See, Evan?" Wat said. "Doesn't it look like a big wheel? Of course, those spokes are really roads and paths Pa can ride over. Then he travels around this big circle."

Evan nodded. "I was never just sure what a minister's circuit was," he admitted.

"Pa, will we have lots of things to do before we go?" Wat asked.

Ma said firmly, "Yes, we'll all be very busy between now and the day we leave."

"You can't go fishing while we work, Wat," Laura added.

Pa didn't say anything. He went out on the porch and down into the yard. The two boys tagged after him. Pa went to the barn and got a spade. When he came back, he looked around the yard and up at the trees. Then he stepped to a spot near the sitting-room window.

"I'm going to plant a young Albemarle pippin right here," he announced. "The tree will grow to shade the west side of the house, and it will give delicious fruit. Those are Virginia's best, spiciest apples."

"Why would your pa want to plant a tree now, when you're leaving?" Evan whispered. "Your family won't get any good from it."

"Other people will. That's what Pa always says. He always plants a tree before we move away from a house."

"It seems queer to me," Evan said slowly, "but it's awfully nice and kind."

Evan's Secret

A FEW days later Jim took his examinations and passed them all. By that time Tom and Kit were both back home, and the family's work had begun. There were lots of things to do around the house and yard before the Reeds moved to their new home in Liberty.

Evan worked almost as hard as Wat, and helped him every morning. Every day about noon, however, he seemed to get a headache. He would feel so bad he'd have to lie down for a while. He told Wat he always felt awfully hot then, too, but he didn't want to tell his mother how sick he really felt. She'd be sure to think he was quite sick. Then he would miss seeing the Reeds off. He made Wat promise not to tell.

Wat said, "You must have the ague. Lots of people in Farmville have it this summer. How do you suppose you caught it?"

"I don't know," Evan said wearily, "but I certainly feel terrible every afternoon. If I tell Ma, she'll make me go to bed and take medicine. She's always buying bottles of it, you know— Peter's Pills, and Compound Extract of Tomato, and the Great Western Fever Panacea, and stuff like that." Evan made a face. Then he brightened a little. "Still, if I do have the ague, maybe I won't have to go to school this fall."

"You'd better go ask Doctor Ed whether you're sick," Wat advised. "If I promise not to tell on you now, will you promise to see him after we leave for Liberty?"

"Yes, but I feel all right every morning," Evan said. "At night, too. It's just in the afternoon

I have a fever. Well, what are we supposed to do this morning?"

"Whitewash the chicken house and the fence."

"To make them look nicer for the new minister?" Evan asked.

"Partly—but partly for the sake of the chickens, too," Wat said. "Whitewash has lime in it, you see, and it kills the lice that get on chickens. Pa told me so."

After the boys had slapped whitewash on the walls of the chicken house, inside and out, they painted the fence. By that time Wat's brothers were laughing at them. Jim said that Wat and Evan looked like speckled chickens themselves. The fence and the chicken house were sparkling white, however.

Two days before Wat's birthday the whole parsonage was clean, from attic to cellar. The windows shone. There were new curtains in the sitting room, and freshly laundered ones at all the other windows. Ma and Bessie Sue had seen to these household things.

Most of the furniture belonged to the parsonage. Ma and Laura had to pack only their clothes and linens. Pa was busy packing all his books and Methodist magazines.

The older boys had mended the roof of the barn. Then they mowed the high weeds that had grown up around the barn.

Wat helped Ma plant a row of jonquil bulbs along the front walk. She said happily, "Think how nice it will be for the new minister's family to see the flowers' golden faces next spring!"

The Bedford County people had promised to send an oxcart for the Reeds' things, and a three-seated carriage for the family to ride in. Tom, who had just returned home, asked Pa if he could travel in the oxcart. Pa said yes. Tom promised to keep an eye on the things in it.

Between jobs for Ma and Pa, Wat was busy

making a fine new bobber for Evan. He had borrowed Jim's best knife and was whittling the bobber out of a chunk of basswood.

When it was finished, Tom said, "It looks perfect, Wat, but why did you put two slots near the bottom instead of one?"

"I thought two might hold a line better than one. I just made up the idea."

"It's smart," Tom said. "I would never have thought of that myself."

Wat was pleased. Tom knew more about fishing than anyone else in the family. If he said the bobber idea was a good one, Evan would surely be pleased.

The last day in Farmville was exciting. The church ladies were preparing a chicken supper for the whole congregation, in honor of the Reeds. They would serve it outside, like a picnic, in the Macbeths' yard.

Wat was the only Reed who was allowed to

help with preparations. This was because he and Evan begged so hard that Mrs. Macbeth gave in.

Wat was trying to help Evan keep his secret. He had promised, but he grew more and more worried about his friend. Evan looked pale and tired, and he was listless. His headache and fever still returned every day at about the same time.

That was always the way with the ague, it seemed. There wasn't anything unusual about it.

Wat and Evan set up the benches and then four long board tables for the picnic supper. They spread white tablecloths on the tables. Evan did his best, but Wat did most of the work. While Evan lay down for a short rest, Wat went to borrow hurricane lamps from all the neighbors to light the yard.

Late in the afternoon members of the congregation began to arrive. Each family brought a big basket of food. Wat and Evan hung around to see what was in the baskets.

Then Mrs. Macbeth called them. She said, "Now you'd better run along home, Wat. It's almost four o'clock. You and Evan must get cleaned up, and I want Evan to do an errand."

"You can't help with it, either," Evan added.

Wat was so surprised he didn't know what to say. This was the time of day Evan usually began to feel better. Why would Evan talk to him that way? Why would he leave him out of something? Wat was rather hurt, but he didn't argue. He walked slowly across the yard to the parsonage, with a queer, unhappy feeling.

A few minutes later he looked out his bedroom window and saw Evan come across the road. He was carrying a covered basket with great care. Mrs. Macbeth met him at the door and took it from him with equal care. Then Evan hurried down the road again.

As Wat dressed he kept glancing out the window. Again he saw Evan come back with a basket, which Mrs. Macbeth took. Once more his friend darted away, and returned a little later with still another basket. What in the world was going on?

Wat was still wondering about the mystery when the Reeds gathered in the sitting room. They were all dressed in their Sunday clothes. Ma looked each one over to be sure that there wasn't a hair out of place.

She herself looked very happy and pretty. She wore a lovely dress made of rosebud material, with a long full skirt. She and Laura put on the bonnets Ma had made. They tied the wide ribbons in big bows under their chins.

Pa looked handsome, too. He wore his long-tailed preaching coat, over a plain white linen shirt. He had a high collar and a wide stock. His high boots were polished till they shone. He put on his tall hat, even though they were going only next door.

Jim's clothes were very much like his father's. The other three boys wore long trousers and short coats. They had small ties, and Ma had found time to make a new white shirt for each of them.

Then she took Pa's arm and they led the way to the party.

Mr. and Mrs. Macbeth met the Reeds as they came across the yard. The Macbeths were the hosts for this party. They greeted the parsonage family just as if they hadn't seen them for days. They led the honor guests to the head table.

Wat was disappointed. "Ma, can't I sit with Evan?" he whispered.

"No, you sit right here by me," Ma said. "And mind your manners."

Wat looked for Evan. He was with some boys from their Sunday-school class. They were whispering together. They looked at Wat, and Evan laughed. Then they found seats together.

Again Wat felt left out. Was Evan mad at him? It wasn't any fun to sit at the head table with just his own family and grownups.

As soon as all the parents and children stood by their places, the minister raised his hand for silence. He bowed his head and said grace. Then the ladies began to bring food out from the Macbeth kitchen.

There were chicken, ham, and wild turkey, and every vegetable Wat could think of. There were biscuits, jellies, and pickles, too. It all tasted so good Wat forgot he was mad at Evan.

Just about the time no one could eat another bite, he saw the boys leave their table. He started to get up and follow them.

"Now, Wat, you just sit still," Ma said to him. "Remember that everyone can see you here at the head table."

Sure enough, everyone was looking at the head table. Everyone was staring at him! Evan, fol-

lowed by three other boys, had marched out of the Macbeth kitchen. Each boy carried a big birthday cake with lighted candles on it. They brought the cakes and put them down in front of Wat. The ladies began to bring out dishes of peach ice cream.

"Surprise! Happy birthday!" shouted the crowd. Then everybody clapped.

Now Wat knew why Evan had acted so

strangely, and why the boys had laughed. This was a surprise party for him!

"This is why I couldn't sit with you," Evan whispered. "Ma was afraid I'd tell you about the surprise."

Mrs. Macbeth was saying, "Wat, blow out all the candles and make your wishes. Then cut one piece of this cake, and do the same for the other three. Afterward we'll take one to each table, and the ladies will finish cutting them."

After Wat had cut the four pieces, someone in the crowd called, "Speech! Speech!"

"Oh, he couldn't make a speech," Wat heard Ma say. "He's only eight."

"Yes, I can, Ma," Wat said excitedly. He stood up. "Thank you all for my birthday cakes. I never saw so many before at one time. I'm going to eat a piece of each of them—if Ma will let me. I'd be pleased if all of you came to visit us in Liberty."

Everyone clapped again. Then everyone ate birthday cake.

After supper the grownups had a good time talking. The children played games like Hunt the Fox and Prisoner's Base.

At nine o'clock, curfew rang. People began to gather up their baskets and lanterns. The Reeds stood in line to say good night and good-by. They shook hands with all their Farmville friends, and Wat thanked each of them for his surprise birthday party.

On Their Way to Liberty

WAT WOKE very early the next morning. The first thing he saw was his bamboo pole, standing in the corner by his bed. He sat up and looked at his sleeping brothers. The four boys shared one large bedroom. Wat climbed out of the big double bed very carefully so he wouldn't waken Kit, who lay with his back to him. In the other big bed Tom and Jim looked as if they were still fast asleep.

"I'd better get out of here before they wake up," Wat thought. "It's really my birthday now. If they catch me, they'll whack me eight times and one to grow on. They all whack hard, too."

Wat pulled on his old clothes and went to the dresser to get his present for Evan.

While Wat's back was turned, Jim opened his eyes, then closed them quickly again. He was playing possum.

Wat shut the dresser drawer as quietly as he could. He tiptoed past the other bed. His bare feet made no noise. He was almost at the door when suddenly he was grabbed from behind.

"So you thought you'd get by without your whacks, did you, sprout?" Jim shouted. His long arms jerked Wat across the bed. "One, two, three——"

Wat kicked and giggled and yelled and fought. Of course this woke Kit. He got up and paddled his brother next.

Finally Tom turned over and yawned. "What's all the fuss?" he asked sleepily. "Oh, yes, Wat's birthday. Come on over to brother Thomas. Come take your medicine."

82

Kit loosened his hold, and Wat jerked away.
He ran out into the hall, down the stairs, and
through the kitchen. He bumped into Bessie Sue
and fled on out the back door. He heard Tom
shouting behind him.

Evan was just coming up to the parsonage.
"Run for the S.H.P.," Wat yelled as he passed
his friend.

Tom came roaring out of the house in time to see them go around the barn. When he rounded the corner, neither was in sight.

"Now you'll get extra whacks," Tom called. "I'll just stand here until you come out—from wherever you are."

Evan nudged Wat and grinned. They were crawling back to their secret hollow. They heard Tom storm about in the barn overhead.

"Just wait till I catch you, Wat Reed!" Tom was shouting.

Soon the boys heard a door bang. Wat and Evan giggled. They knew Tom hadn't meant to stay in the barn long. Now they felt safe.

SKUNK PARADE

Wat's eyes were getting used to the half-light. When he glanced down he noticed the sort of tracks he and Evan had seen before. Wat leaned over and studied them. "It's not a dog," he decided. "In a dog's track only four toes show. This animal has five. It doesn't have any claws on its hind feet, either."

"Sure?" Evan asked.

"Sure. I looked at your Blackie's prints just the other day."

"Well, before the animal comes back," Evan said, "I've got a present for you."

"I have one for you, too." Wat reached into his pants pocket.

"It's not my birthday!" Evan said, looking up at Wat in surprise.

"I know, but you're my best friend. I want to give you a present before I move away."

"It's my turn first. Shut your eyes and hold out your hand," Evan commanded.

When Wat opened his eyes he found himself holding a bobber. Red, yellow, and blue stripes were painted on it.

"I made it myself," Evan said proudly. "I painted it to remind you of sunfish."

"Thank you," Wat said quickly. "Thanks a lot, Evan. Now it's your turn to shut your eyes and hold out your hand."

Evan did as he was told. When he opened his eyes a new bobber lay on his palm, too.

Both boys burst out laughing.

Finally Wat said, "I made your present, too. I didn't think of painting it. But I carved your initials—see?"

When he showed Evan the double slot at the bottom, Evan said it was much better than any old "boughten" one. "Would we have time to try them out?" he asked.

"I'm afraid not——" Wat began regretfully.

Just then they heard Tom call, "In free, Wat!" as if they were playing a game. "Breakfast's ready. Come on, you win. I'll not give you those extra whacks after all."

The boys started to crawl forward. Then Wat stopped at the sound of crackling leaves.

"That must be Kit," he whispered. "He's the only other one who knows about the S.H.P. He's already paddled me." He called loudly, "We're back here, Kit. Is it safe for us to come out now?"

Kit didn't answer.

"Is Tom still waiting?" Evan called.

Still Kit didn't answer. The rustling had stopped by now.

Evan started forward again, but Wat grabbed his arm and pointed straight ahead of them. There, not far away, were a mother skunk and five young ones. The skunks were staring at the boys. Wat and Evan froze. Hardly breathing, they kept very still.

"Maybe those boys went fishing," they heard Bessie Sue call. "Wat had a bobber with him when he ran into me."

"I don't think so," Kit shouted. "His pole's still upstairs."

Mrs. Skunk turned her head at this noise. The little skunks turned their heads, too. Wat and Evan knew better than to move at all.

A few minutes later Jim blew his whistle. Kit shouted, "Breakfast! Come on, Wat."

Then everything was quiet outside the barn. "Let's go," Evan whispered.

Wat shook his head. Even when Laura called, "Wat, Pa says for you to come now!" he was afraid to move. Mrs. Skunk was washing one of her babies, but she kept an eye on the boys.

Wat didn't move, but he could at least look around. He stared again at the strange tracks he had seen earlier. They led right to the skunks.

"Why, of course, that's what they are!" Wat thought excitedly. "Skunk tracks!"

Someone was coming toward the S.H.P. now. Mrs. Skunk raised her bushy tail.

88

"I'm glad they're looking at us instead of away from us," Wat muttered to Evan.

"If that's Kit and he comes in here, they'll turn around," Evan said. "Then you and I'll be skunky the rest of our lives."

Outside, Kit called, "Oh, come on, Wat. Your breakfast is getting cold. I'd have come sooner, but I didn't want the others to find out about the S.H.P. Though I guess that doesn't make much difference now."

Mrs. Skunk turned to face the entrance. Her tail was still high. The little skunks turned their backs to the boys. Wat knew what might happen next. He held his breath.

"Have it your own way," Kit shouted, as he ran off. For a few minutes everyone under the barn was very still. Then Mrs. Skunk lowered her tail. She started toward the entrance. Her babies followed her. The skunk family filed out of the S.H.P. Evan started to leave, too.

"Wait a minute," Wat said. "Something might scare them back."

Evan didn't answer. He was already crawling out of the entrance.

"I'll be right back as soon as I eat breakfast," he called over his shoulder, and ran on home.

As Wat crawled out of the S.H.P., he saw Kit sitting on the back steps. He was laughing so hard he had to hold his sides. "Oh, Wat," he gasped, "the S.H.P. was sure crowded this morning. I never saw anything so funny as you and Evan bringing up the rear of that skunk parade. Six skunks! No wonder you didn't come in to eat breakfast when we called you."

GOOD-BY TO FARMVILLE

Kit and Wat were giggling so hard they staggered into the dining room. The family looked at them in amazement.

"Where have you been, Wat Reed?" Laura scolded. "Did you run off to go fishing?"

Everything seemed funny to the boys now. Laura's question set them off again.

Pa frowned and Ma looked worried. Only Jim gave them a little smile. "Calm down, boys," he said quietly. "What happened?"

Kit could hardly tell the story, for laughing. Before he was halfway through, even Pa was smiling broadly. When he had finished, everybody howled.

Wat began to eat his breakfast. Suddenly they heard a noise on the front porch.

"Maybe your six skunks followed you," Laura teased. Everyone laughed again.

"It's probably Evan," said Wat. "He told me he'd come over again."

Bessie Sue said from the door, "The man's out in front with the oxcart, Reverend. I'd better get this table cleared right away."

"Yes," Pa said. "We must all get to work."

For a little while there was a bustle around the parsonage. Ma and Bessie Sue made sure that they were leaving everything in order. The boys carried out the Reeds' belongings and loaded them in the cart. The cart would take everything but what they would need on their journey. The three-seated carriage in which the family would travel had arrived, too.

Evan wandered over. He stood watching unhappily as the Reed boys brought out boxes and trunks and stowed them in the cart. In less than an hour it was ready to start. Tom climbed up on it. "Good-by, everybody!" he shouted. "See you in Liberty!" The oxen strained and the cart moved forward.

"Good-by, Tom!" everybody cried.

Wat turned to Pa. "Is there time for me to try my new birthday bobber?"

"Mercy, no, child!" Ma interrupted. "We'll

be leaving just as soon as we can say good-by to everyone."

Some of Laura's friends had come to see her off. Mr. and Mrs. Macbeth and other neighbors gathered around the carriage. Kit and Jim carried out a few things that remained to be stowed in it. Wat brought out his fishing pole.

Pa saddled Queenie, led her around, and tied her to the hitching post.

Then he and Ma closed the door of the parsonage. They shook hands with all their friends. Evan and Wat stood together, but they couldn't think of anything to say to each other.

"We must be off," Pa said at last. He helped Ma and Laura into the carriage. Bessie Sue came next. The driver climbed up to his seat.

"Wat, you climb up on the front seat with Mr. Pond," said Pa. "After the first few miles, you may ride Queenie. After all, it's your birthday, and you deserve some special treat."

"Pa! Oh, Pa, that's wonderful!" Wat scrambled up beside the driver. His brothers got in, and Pa mounted Queenie.

The carriage started. Evan ran down the road alongside of it. He called, "I almost forgot—happy birthday, Wat!"

"Thanks, Evan. Don't forget your promise about seeing Doctor Ed. I want you to visit me next summer sure."

The carriage was gaining speed. Evan stopped running. "Will if I can," he called.

He waved, and Wat waved his fishing pole. "Good-by! Good-by, Evan!"

Young Reed

In the afternoon, ten days later, the Reeds first saw the Peaks of Otter. Mr. Pond had told the boys story after story about these mountains. His great-grandfather had pioneered here over a hundred years before.

Wat liked to listen to Mr. Pond's stories. He was a mountaineer and could tell thrilling tales.

Mr. Pond pulled the horses to a quick stop. He stood up and waved his whip excitedly toward the Peaks.

"There they are, like I told you," he said proudly. "Look at the tops a-shinin' gold. Means a long stretch o' good weather."

Wat sat up straight and stared at the mountains. "I'd like to climb right up to the top of the tallest one and see what's on the other side!"

"It'll be Sharp Top or Flat Top you'll be wanting to climb." Mr. Pond pointed with his whip. "Some of the Peaks are about four thousand feet high. Better wait a spell before you try climbing one."

"But that's not even a mile," Kit said quickly. "Wat and I have walked twice that far a lot of times. Wat's always wandering off somewhere to fish."

"Mountain climbing's a cat of another color from walking," Mr. Pond said with a laugh. "You don't get very far very fast. It takes a lot of breath and patience to climb a mountain." He flicked the reins. "Get up, Star. Pull your share, Bonnie."

"What's that over there, Mr. Pond?" Jim called. He pointed to a lane shut off from the main road by a gate.

"That's Poplar Forest, Mr. Jefferson's old home. Many's the time that fine gentleman came here to rest when he was the third President of the United States."

"I thought he lived at Monticello, near Charlottesville," Jim put in.

"Likely he did," Mr. Pond said, "but he built

Poplar Forest right here in our foothills, too. Folks called him the Squire. He had fine friends and a lot of land—over four thousand acres in his farm."

They passed the gate of Poplar Forest but could not see the house. It was set far back from the road. Wat decided he would come out here and explore. If only Evan could come along!

They were coming near Liberty now. Ma and Laura straightened their bonnets. Bessie Sue had been dozing. She woke up with a start when Kit told her they were near Liberty. The boys put on their stockings and boots. Pa rode up close to the carriage and asked Mr. Pond to stop. Then he and Wat changed places. It was time for the minister to put on his long-skirted coat and high hat.

When they started up again, Wat rode close to the carriage. He didn't want to miss any of Mr. Pond's stories.

Pa asked the driver to slow down as they drew near a square, two-storied brick building.

"Kit! Wat!" Pa raised his voice. "There's where you'll be going to school."

Everybody turned to look at the schoolhouse as they passed by. In its big fenced-in yard a group of boys was marching. A dark-haired lad gave the orders in a ringing voice.

"What are they doing?" Wat asked, riding close to Mr. Pond's side of the carriage.

"They're drilling," Mr. Pond answered. "They call themselves the Piedmont School Militia. That building there's the Piedmont Academy. They've been drilling with those wooden guns real regular lately."

Mr. Reed looked puzzled. "Why?" he asked.

"They're copying the Bedford County Militia—the best-trained soldiers in Virginia."

Pa shook his head. "Why, even the children are thinking of war!"

Wat fell behind to watch the boys for a minute. Then he trotted after the carriage. "It might be sort of fun to go there to school," he said to himself. He thought it would be great to belong to the boys' militia.

"Those Yankees can't tell us what to do. We can fight," Mr. Pond was saying to Pa, as Wat caught up. "They'll see."

"Yes, and I'm old enough to go as soon as the fighting starts," Jim said quickly.

Ma didn't say a word, but she looked worried.

"I'm afraid you're right, Mr. Pond," Pa said sadly. "There might be fighting soon. It's too bad the states can't think alike. It will be a terrible thing if they are forced to settle their differences with bloodshed."

Pa had a way of saying things that made them sound serious. Everyone rode in silence for the next few minutes.

"Tell us a little bit about Liberty, Mr. Pond,"

Ma said at last. "There's been too much talk of fighting." Her voice sounded cheery, but there was a worried look on her face.

"We're just starting down Main Street now, Mrs. Reed," he answered. "Liberty is a mighty nice town. Nice folks and churches. There's a girls' school besides the Piedmont Academy for boys." He paused to give the horses a flick. "Back at the Academy, that was Charlie Jennings leading the militia. His father is the doctor in our town."

Mr. Pond flicked the reins again. The carriage rolled on down Main Street and through the center of town.

Suddenly Kit said, "Look, there's Tom! That must be our new house!"

Laura and Ma waved to Tom. Bessie Sue waved to him, too.

"Who's that young man talking to Tom, Mr. Pond?" asked Ma.

"Frank Stone," said Mr. Pond. "He lives across the road from you all. Frank just got into the Bedford County Militia. For an eighteen-year-old, he's one of the best riders in this part of the state."

Mr. Pond pulled the horses up at the parsonage. Tom and Frank hurried to meet them.

"Hi, Tom! Hi, Tom!" Everyone was shouting greetings.

Tom gave his mother a big hug. "Ma, you ought to see inside the house! The church ladies have worked hard to fix it up just right. They've made me feel right at home. The Stones have had me over for meals."

"It may not be so big as our last home, but it does look pleasant and homelike," Ma said. Then she smiled at Frank.

"Oh, I almost forgot," Tom said. "Ma, Pa, this is Frank Stone. His father and mother are coming right over to meet you."

Frank shook hands with everyone and said hello to Mr. Pond.

The family was eager to see the house. So Mr. Pond said good-by. "Stick to your fishing instead of trying to climb those mountains right away," he told Wat.

Wat grinned and waved good-by to Mr. Pond. Then he hurried into the house after the others.

"Come on, everybody, and look around," Tom said. "Pa, here's your study. Look at the space for your books. There's a big room upstairs where two of us can sleep. The other bedrooms are downstairs. The dining room is the best room. It's the biggest of all."

Wat and Kit hurried from one room to the next. The others followed along behind. Tom was right. It was a nice house. Wat raced ahead, to the room upstairs.

"Kit, look!" Wat called. "You can see the Peaks from this window."

"Maybe you and I could have this room under the eaves," Kit said. "Maybe we could make a new Secret Hiding Place up here!"

TWO NEW FRIENDS

A few hours later people began to come to greet the new pastor and his wife. Each brought some food—fresh-baked bread, or a pie, or cookies, or a cake. The Reverend and Mrs. Reed were very busy talking to their new friends.

"Bessie Sue, please tell Ma I'll be back soon," Wat said. His brothers had gone off to look at one of the huge warehouses where tobacco leaves were dried and stored. Wat wanted to visit another place right away.

He ran out the back door, around the house, and headed toward the school. He was going to watch the Piedmont School Militia drill!

It was a long walk. It hadn't seemed so far

105

when he was riding Queenie. When he reached the school, all the boys were hurrying out the gate with their books slung over their shoulders.

"I wish I hadn't missed the drill!" Wat said to himself, disappointed. He dug his hands into his pockets and turned to start back.

Then the dark-haired boy who was the leader of the militia called out, "You're one of the Reeds, aren't you?" He ran across the yard and held out his hand. "I saw you riding by with Mr. Pond. My name is Charlie Jennings."

"I'm Wat." Wat smiled as he shook Charlie's hand. "I came back to watch you march. Could Kit and I join your militia?"

"We'd be glad to have you." Charlie grinned. "If you'd like, I'll ride you home double on my horse, Gypsy. First I have to get my schoolbooks. Won't you come inside with me?"

Wat nodded, and the two boys hurried up the steps together. When they reached the schoolroom, Charlie motioned for Wat to wait outside in the hallway.

"Mr. Proctor teaches two grades in this room, the third grade and my grade, the fourth," Charlie whispered. "He's busy correcting papers at his desk now. We can't disturb him." Quietly Charlie went in and picked up his books.

Mr. Proctor didn't look up. Wat could see that he was a small man with black hair and side whiskers. He wore a high white stock.

Suddenly Mr. Proctor said aloud, "Come in, young Reed."

Wat was surprised. As he entered, Mr. Proctor asked, "What is your given name?"

"Wat, sir," Wat answered, swallowing hard.

"I presume that your given name is Walter," said Mr. Proctor clearly. "At the Piedmont Academy we refer to people, places, and things by their true names. In what grade were you enrolled in your last school?"

"I finished the third grade in Farmville, sir," Wat said. "I'm ready for the fourth now. I'm eight, going on nine," he added proudly.

"You are much too young for the fourth grade," Mr. Proctor said. "You will start here in the third grade. I will so advise your father. He wrote and asked that you be entered here as soon as possible."

Wat hesitated. He didn't think Mr. Proctor was being fair. However, he knew Ma and Pa wouldn't want him to argue with his teacher.

"Do not be tardy on Monday morning," Mr. Proctor added. "Good day."

The minute they were outside, Wat said, "I know I'm ready for the fourth grade. What difference does my age make?"

"All the boys in the fourth grade are nine—like me," answered Charlie. "Come on. Let's get Gypsy. I'll tell you all about school on the way home."

108

The small black horse whinnied when she saw Charlie coming. She was tied to a long rail fence at the end of the schoolyard.

"What a beauty!" Wat cried.

"I raised her myself from a colt," Charlie said proudly. "Gypsy, shake hands with Wat."

The little mare shook her head up and down and pawed the ground. Then she lifted her right foot daintily.

Wat's eyes sparkled as he shook it. Then he laughed. "Gypsy is the second new friend I've found today!"

On the way home Wat thought hard about Mr. Proctor. He would show Mr. Proctor what he could do.

When the boys got to the parsonage, Wat slid off Gypsy's back. He gave her a friendly pat and said good-by to Charlie.

"I'll meet you at school early Monday morning, Wat," called Charlie as he rode away.

Wat ran into the house to tell Pa all about his visit at the school. When he had finished, he asked, "What shall I do, Pa? I know the *Third Reader* by heart. I don't think it's fair to keep me out of the fourth grade just because I'm not so old as the other boys."

Mr. Reed looked at the determined boy standing before him.

"Where there's a will, there's a way, my boy," he said. "I know Mr. Proctor is a good teacher. Bide your time and maybe you'll be able to prove what you can do."

That night Kit and Wat climbed the stairs to the room under the eaves.

"I have a new motto, Kit," Wat announced. "Pa gave me the idea. It's 'Where there's a will, there's a way.' I'll find the way to get into the fourth grade somehow!"

The Friday Exercises

EARLY MONDAY morning, Wat and Charlie ran up the front steps of the schoolhouse together. Kit was in another classroom with the fifth-grade boys.

Wat and Charlie hurried into their classroom. Charlie said his grade was doing something special today. Wat was eager to find out what. They saw the fourth grade bunched around Mr. Proctor's desk. The boys were staring at something on the desk top.

"That old spider looks as big as a dragon!" one boy said excitedly.

Wat stood on tiptoe so that he might see the

111

spider, too. "Do you have a special kind of spider in Liberty, Charlie?" .

Charlie laughed. "No, but this is why I wanted to get to school early today. My grade is studying natural history, so the class brought in spiders, bees, and houseflies. See, I've brought two mosquitoes myself!"

Carefully Charlie unfolded a bit of paper. Each mosquito was stuck to the paper with a tiny bit of flour paste. He explained that he had mounted them this way so that he could save them for his insect collection.

"I wish I might study nature, too," Wat said wistfully. "I bet it's harder but more interesting than spelling or anything else."

"Mr. Proctor said we could look at these insects under his magnifying glass," Charlie said. Wat had never seen a magnifying glass before.

"May I take a closer look?" Wat asked.

David Hughes, a big boy in Charlie's class,

pushed ahead of Wat. "This is just for fourth-graders," David said abruptly.

Mr. Proctor, who had been standing near by, rapped on the desk.

"Attention, class! Walter Reed's curiosity is to be admired, not brushed aside. I want you to pay close attention to what you see today. The fourth-grade composition assignment for the week will be based upon it. You will write about the magnifying glass and the microscope. As usual, the best composition will be read aloud before both classes at our Friday exercises."

"Now may I see Charlie's mosquitoes, Mr. Proctor?" Wat asked shyly. He was so interested in the magnifying glass, he forgot all about the rude boy.

"Certainly," Mr. Proctor answered.

Wat looked eagerly through the small glass. Now, with his eye closer to it, he could see the enlarged mosquito much more clearly. He pulled back in amazement. "It sure looks as if it's grown!" he said excitedly.

Several of the boys snickered. Mr. Proctor frowned. "Young gentlemen! Walter is a new boy in our school," he said sharply. "You should at least be polite."

"Come on, Wat," whispered Charlie. "Your class doesn't have to write the composition. You can look through the magnifying glass again later. I'll show you the dictionary, where we look up credit words."

"Credit words? What are they?"

"It's simple. Every new word we hear or see we write down as best we can at the time. Then, at school, we look up how to spell it and what it means. Mr. Proctor gives us a credit point for each correct word in our notebook at the end of the week."

"Is that all!" Wat didn't think this sounded very important.

"Oh, no! It's like a game," Charlie answered. "At the end of the month the boy who has the most credit points in each grade gets a better seat in the room. He moves back one seat. Right now I have the back seat in my grade. It's best because it's farthest from Proccie's nose. I have to keep ahead of everyone else in my class or I'll lose my place."

"I understand," Wat said. "It's a sort of race. Why did Proccie start it?"

"Oh, he said the boys with the most credits were those he could trust most."

Wat followed Charlie to a long table against one wall of the room. A bookcase was near the table. "The dictionary and the encyclopedia volumes and all the books in that bookcase belong to Mr. Proctor."

"Why, he has more books than Pa!" Wat exclaimed in surprise.

"Seventy-eight. I counted them one time. I

guess we're lucky to have Mr. Proctor even if he is such a hard teacher," Charlie said. He showed Wat how to use the dictionary.

Wat thought this was easy. His Pa had shown him how to use the index in one of his books. The words in the dictionary were listed in the same way, in alphabetical order.

"These books don't have lists of words like the dictionary." Charlie pointed to the volumes of the encyclopedia. "They have pieces, or articles, about all sorts of different subjects."

"I wonder how long it would take me to read every article in every volume," Wat wondered.

Just then one of the boys rang the school bell. It was time for class to begin. Wat was given the front seat in the third-grade row, since he was a new boy.

"Third-grade spelling first," Mr. Proctor announced. "Walter, you will take down the spelling words on your slate, as the other boys do.

116

You may remember some of the words from your schoolwork in Farmville."

Spelling was easy for Wat. He had always had high marks, and today he got a hundred. "If I keep on doing well, maybe Mr. Proctor will let me be in the fourth grade!" he thought.

Arithmetic and reading were easy for him, too. He recited correctly and then finished the assignments quickly. Mr. Proctor gave him permission to look at the books in the bookcase and on the table.

In one of the encyclopedia volumes he found an article on the microscope. Before he had finished reading it, one of the fourth-graders needed the book for his composition.

Wat returned to his seat. He sat for a minute, dreaming about all the wonderful things that could be seen under the lens of a microscope. How he wished he were in Charlie's grade! Then he could read about scientific subjects. Then he could study natural history. Suddenly he sat up straight, his eyes sparkling.

"I've found the way!" he whispered to himself. "I know how I will prove to Proccie what I can do."

A FOURTH-GRADE FIGHTER

On Friday the boys wore their best suits to school. This was the day visitors came to listen to the exercises. Wat's mother had to call on a sick friend. So she was not there today.

First there were recitations by two of the boys. Then there was singing, followed by a spelling bee and ciphering races. The ciphering, when the boys were adding sums as fast as they could, were the most exciting races, Wat thought.

Finally Mr. Proctor took a composition from his desk drawer. He cleared his throat and began, "It is our custom to close the Friday exercises with the recitation of the best composition by a fourth-grade student."

Wat looked at Charlie. He hoped Charlie's paper would win. Still, David Hughes had boasted about how good his piece was. David said he was sure his paper would be chosen.

"Our theme for today is on the magnifying glass and the microscope," Mr. Proctor was saying. Suddenly he looked at Wat. "This week a boy in the third grade asked if he might turn in a fourth-grade composition. I consider it the best paper of all those I received. The research work done was thorough and accurate. The boy who did this paper reads and writes well. Walter Reed, please come forward."

Wat felt dazed by the sudden announcement. He hadn't tried to outdo the older boys. He had just tried to do his best, to show Mr. Proctor that he could do fourth-grade work.

He walked slowly to the front of the room and

took his paper from Mr. Proctor. In an unsteady voice Wat said, " 'The Magnifying Glass and the Microscope' is the title." He looked up and saw Charlie smile at him. Now he felt more certain of himself. He started to read. " 'Magnifying glasses have been used for at least two thousand years. A simple microscope is generally called a magnifying glass. It is a very simple lens. A more complicated microscope has more than one lens. It makes things seem much larger than one magnifying glass does.' " As Wat continued to read his paper, the other boys listened quietly.

After Wat had finished, Mr. Proctor said, "Your paper was excellent, Walter. I noted, too, that you used a good many credit words. Perhaps you will have earned a new seat by the end of the month."

Wat thanked Mr. Proctor and went to take his seat, but he was determined to earn more than just a new seat. He wanted to learn more and more. He would work so hard that Mr. Proctor would put him in the fourth grade.

"How many credit words did you use in that paper?" David Hughes growled, as Wat passed.

Wat knew he shouldn't stop to talk. Mr. Proctor was waiting for him to take his seat before closing the exercises.

"Think you're pretty smart, don't you?" David muttered when Wat went on without a word. "You'll soon see how smart I think you are!" David added, more loudly.

"Silence! Silence!" Mr. Proctor ordered. Then he closed the exercises and thanked the visitors for coming.

After school was out, Wat found David waiting for him down in the yard.

"Teacher's pet! Teacher's pet!" David jeered. "You think you're so smart that you don't even have to speak when you're spoken to."

Wat was taken aback. He stopped dead still

and looked at David in amazement. "I don't," Wat cried. "That isn't so!"

"You wrote that paper just to show off," David accused Wat. "You wanted to make me look like a dunce. Didn't you?"

"I did not! That's not true!" Wat knew David was being unfair. Before he could say any more, David gave him a shove, tripped him, and he sprawled. The bigger boy stood over him with fists clenched.

Finally David stepped back. He thought he had given the new boy a good scare. "Guess you aren't so smart as you thought you were," he taunted. He picked up his books and papers. Then he turned and walked toward the gate. After a few steps he turned around and called, "You can get up now, Teacher's Pet."

In a second Wat was on his feet. His head down, bent low, he rushed straight toward David. He'd make the boy take back his words!

122

Wat was small for his age, but he was strong. He caught David in a tackle around the knees and hung on, though David flailed at his head and shoulders. Wat locked his arms tighter and David lost his balance and fell backward.

In a flash Wat lunged forward. Now he was astride the boy's chest, pinning down his arms. David couldn't use his fists, and kicking did him no good.

Wat could have punched his face. But somehow he didn't feel so angry now that he had brought David down.

"Take back that name you called me," Wat said, gasping.

David shook his head. His hair was tousled and most of the buttons had popped off his shirt. He wiggled and twisted, but he still couldn't push Wat off.

Suddenly Wat leaned over and grabbed some long stalks of grass. He began to tickle David's

face with them while he chanted, "Take it back, take it back——"

David couldn't help giggling. "All right," he said weakly. "I take it back. You didn't mean to be Proccie's pet."

When the boys got to their feet, Wat's clothes were as rumpled, torn, and dirty as David's. Wat had bitten his lip and it was bleeding, and there was a big bump on his forehead.

Wat stuck out his hand, and David shook it. "You're a fourth-grade fighter," David said with respect. "I'll say that for you."

THE WAY IS FOUND

When Wat reached home, his lip was still bleeding. He hated to have Ma see how badly torn his best coat was. She would be disappointed in him. He was worried, too, about what Pa would say when he learned about the fight.

Ma was very unhappy when she saw Wat. Kit told him he looked awful. Pa frowned, but he gave Wat a chance to tell them what had happened. Wat didn't say that David Hughes had bragged a lot. He just told his parents that David had called him a teacher's pet.

Kit asked why. He wanted the whole story. So Wat told all that had occurred at the exercises. Kit said that proved the fight was David's fault.

Ma said nothing, but Wat could tell she didn't approve of fighting, no matter how good the cause. Without a word she bathed Wat's face and put salve on the cut. Then she made a poultice to help reduce the bump on his forehead. The pack felt soothing to Wat.

As she worked, Pa said, "I'm sorry about Wat's coat, Pharaba, but I know you can mend the rip. It's high time the boy learned to take care of himself."

Wat looked at his father in surprise. "Why,

Pa," he said, "I thought you'd be cross with me. I thought you didn't approve of fighting."

"I don't," Mr. Reed answered. "I'm always sorry to see men come to blows over any matter. However, you didn't start this fight. You were attacked unfairly.

"I believe it's better to settle arguments peacefully," he went on, "but sometimes there's no other course but physical force."

Though his face hurt and his whole body was beginning to ache, Wat felt pleased. His father had called him a man!

Now he would work harder than ever to get ahead in school. He had already decided what he would do next.

That night he took Kit's old fourth-grade books from the shelf. He spread them out on the sitting-room table along with his own third-grade reader and speller.

"I'm going to do the assignments for both

grades," he told his brothers. "I'll catch up with the fourth-graders. Then I'll ask Mr. Proctor to let me recite with them. If I show him I can do the work and keep up with the class, surely he'll let me move!"

Kit nodded. "After all, if you do all that extra studying you ought to be in the fourth."

"If you don't watch out," Tom joked, "you'll catch up with Jim in college."

Wat worked very hard, but it took him more than a month to catch up. Then one Monday he went to school early.

Mr. Proctor was sitting at his desk reading. Wat put his assignment for the day on the left side of the desk where the third-grade boys always laid their homework. Then he placed some papers on the fourth-grade pile.

When Mr. Proctor looked up, Wat asked, "May I try to recite with the fourth grade, sir?"

Several boys were already in their seats. They

had heard his question and looked up, curious to hear the teacher's answer.

Mr. Proctor's eyes twinkled. "Young Reed, after your first week here, I thought you could do fourth-grade work. I wondered how long it would take before you thought you had proved it to me. Because of your age, the third grade seemed a better place for you."

Wat looked disappointed.

"However," Mr. Proctor went on, "you have worked hard and done the assignments well. The composition you did that first week deserved the commendation it received. Of course you had more time to work on it than the boys in the fourth. They worked on their regular assignments while you wrote your theme."

"I know," Wat quickly agreed. "David thought I wanted to be a teacher's pet, but I didn't want that at all. I just wanted to learn new things—not the same things I already knew."

Mr. Proctor smiled at Wat's serious look. "Put the third-grade books away, Walter. Willy Nimo, you may move back one seat. Walter Reed is joining your grade."

"Now we can race for credit words," Charlie whispered as Wat came to take his seat. "I got that word 'commendation.' Bet you didn't!"

Wat grinned and gave Charlie a wink.

Wat Takes Over

IT WAS a cold rainy evening in late November of 1862. The Reeds had lived in Blackstone now for two months. It was a railroad town southeast of Farmville and Liberty.

Before they left Liberty, Wat had helped Pa plant a tree in front of the old parsonage. This time, moving had made Wat sad. Pa had worried more and more over the talk of war.

Then war between the states had come in earnest with the attack on Fort Sumter. That had been a year ago last April. The Bedford Militia had marched away to join the Virginia forces. They were fighting now. Frank Stone was with

131

them. Charlie and the other boys in the Piedmont Militia were acting as a home guard.

Jim Reed had enlisted almost at the start. Tom had followed shortly before the family moved to Blackstone. Ma and Pa had said he was too young, but Tom was determined to go.

Wat missed having these two brothers around. Now that Laura was married, Wat and Kit were the only children left at home.

A letter from Tom had come last week, but it had been a long time since they had had any word from Jim. Sadly Wat watched the lines of anxiety deepen in his mother's face.

Pa was away from home much of the time. He said that in these terrible times the people of his churches needed his help and advice more than they ever had before.

This November evening Mrs. Reed tied her bonnet strings under her chin and picked up a basket of food from the table. As she pulled her warm cape about her shoulders, she turned to Wat and Kit.

"I'm sorry Bessie Sue had to go up to Farmville," she said. "However, her father's very ill and needs her. Wat, are you sure you and Kit can manage for a few days by yourselves?"

"Ma, we're not babies any more!" Wat said.

Kit laughed. "We can take care of everything, Ma. Don't you worry."

A boy with a rickety wagon and a thin mule waited outside for Mrs. Reed. The Blackstone doctor would be gone for another week, and the boy's family wanted help badly. Ma knew the Havens. They went to one of Pa's churches. She had offered to help Mrs. Haven care for the boy's little brothers and sisters, who were ill.

"I'll carry your basket out to the wagon, Ma," Wat said, as he took the basket from her. "It's too heavy for you. There must be enough food here for two families!"

"It's little enough to cheer a family in these troubled times," Ma said. "Some nourishment may make them feel better and stronger."

The boys hurried down the walk from the house with Ma. The rain had eased up, but the dampness and cold made Wat shiver. The boys waved to Johnny Haven.

When they reached the wagon, Ma said, "I won't be too far away. The Havens' farm is near by. If a letter comes from Jim, please bring it out to me. I wouldn't worry so, if I knew he was all right."

"We'll bring it, Ma!" the boys called as Ma and Johnny drove off.

They brought in a few extra pieces of wood. Then they spread their books out on the dining-room table and began to study. Pa said they should keep up with their studies even though there was a war. The house seemed empty and strangely quiet without Ma. Suddenly Wat put his books down. He thought he heard a mysterious sound.

"What's that noise?" he asked. "Kit, there's something on the porch!" They listened, scarcely daring to breathe.

There was a scraping noise, then a faint knock at the door.

"Come on!" Wat said.

"Be careful, Wat," Kit warned. "Perhaps it's a trick. Might be a Yankee scout."

Cautiously Wat opened the door a crack. A man in a torn, muddy, gray uniform almost fell in on him. A gray coat was hanging loosely from his shoulders.

"Jim!" Wat gasped, as his arms went out to help his brother.

"Jim, you're hurt!" Kit cried.

"Hello, sprouts," Jim mumbled. "Don't scare Ma." Then he fainted.

Wat and Kit supported him to the sitting room

and got him onto the sofa. Then Kit stayed with him, while Wat ran to get a basin of water.

"I'd better put some water on to heat," Wat thought. "Ma always says a hot cup of tea is good for someone who's sick."

He carefully carried a basin of cool water to the sitting room. He wiped Jim's forehead and cheeks with a wet rag. In a little while Jim opened his eyes. He smiled weakly, then closed his eyes again.

"Where's Ma—Pa?" Jim moaned. "My arm hurts. Shot—at Sharpsburg. Been in hospital—walked home." His teeth were chattering and he was shivering.

Kit ran to get a quilt. Wat told Jim not to talk. He explained that Ma was helping the Havens and that Pa would be away on circuit for a few days. When Kit came back, Wat remembered the water he had put on to heat. "I'll make you some pennyroyal tea, Jim," he said.

"That's a good idea," Kit said.

The pennyroyal leaves were in Ma's herb chest. Wat sprinkled a few of the dried leaves in a cup and added the hot water. When he came back to the sitting room, he let the tea cool a little. Then he spooned it into Jim's mouth.

Jim looked directly at Wat, but didn't seem to know him. Then Jim tried to get up, but the boys gently pushed him back. Wat tucked the quilt around Jim again.

"I'd better run and get Dr. Wilson," Kit said with a worried frown.

"He's out of town," Wat reminded him. "That's why Ma's taking care of the Havens."

Kit's face was pale. "Jim's so sick I—I forgot. You're better with sick people than I am." He went to get his coat. "I'll go for Ma. At least I can do that. She will have to leave the Havens for a while."

"I'll try to look after Jim alone till you get

back," Wat said. He put his hand on Jim's fore-head. It felt hot. "I think he has a fever, Kit," he went on.

"I'll hurry as fast as I can," Kit called as he went out the door.

"I'll do the best I can till Ma comes," Wat called after him.

When Kit snapped the door shut, Jim sat up. "It's hot in here—too warm. Open a window." He stirred restlessly. "My arm—my arm——"

"Ma's coming soon," Wat said. "Do you want a drink?"

"Water," Jim whispered.

As he got the water, Wat thought of what he should do next to make Jim more comfortable. He tried to think of what Charlie's father, Dr. Jennings, would do. Charlie had told Wat how his father used poultices and salves on wounds. Ma had used them, too.

"I'll have to be the doctor," Wat thought,

"until Ma can get here. She'll know what's best. She's helped a lot of sick people."

Wat propped Jim up with a pillow and gave him the cup of water. He knew Jim's arm must hurt terribly. Jim was always brave and never complained. Wat knew he must do something to give Jim relief!

Then he decided. "Jim," he said quietly, "I'm going to wash your wound and put a flaxseed poultice on it. That's what Ma did when I fell and cut up my knees so bad once."

Jim mumbled something, but Wat couldn't understand what he said.

Wat got a pan of warm water and put it on the floor beside the sofa. Then he put a clean cloth in it to soak. When he pulled back the quilt, he saw that Jim's shirt sleeve was ripped across. Jim's left arm was missing below the elbow. Part of Jim's arm had been amputated!

Jim moaned again. Wat tried to be very gentle

as he took the old bandages from the wound. The shirt was so torn that it was easy to fold it out of the way.

Wat's hand trembled. It took all his courage to go on, but he had to do his best to help Jim feel better.

First, he washed the wound, which had not healed over. Then he ran to the herb chest and took out a box of flaxseeds. Using the last hot water in the kettle, he poured a little into a pan and added the seeds. He stirred it. Soon the mixture was a soft paste.

He spread the flaxseed jelly in the center of a clean cloth. He remembered clearly what he had seen Ma do next. He folded the cloth so that it made a flat, square package. Then he placed the poultice on Jim's wound and tied it gently in place with a strip of cloth.

"There!" Wat sighed. "Lie quiet, Jim." He knew the poultice would be soothing, but Jim

141

would have to be still so that it would stay in place. Wat pulled the blanket over his brother. Then he sat down in Ma's rocker to wait.

Jim's eyes were closed, but he moved his head restlessly from side to side. Wat watched him anxiously. Jim still had a fever, but Wat knew he had done all he could.

Now Jim was muttering. His voice sounded strained and unnatural. "Here come those Yanks again. Hold 'em, boys! General Lee says don't let them take this sunken road."

Wat realized that Jim was out of his head. He thought he was back at Sharpsburg, in the terrible battle by Antietam Creek. "Easy now, Jim," Wat said. "You're home. We'll look after you. Just lie still."

Jim kept muttering: "We mow them down, but still they come. The West Wood was bad, but this is worse. Never saw so many of our boys hit——" His voice died away.

142

Suddenly he started up and gave a sharp cry. "Oh, my arm! They got me that time." He fell back on the pillow.

With soothing hands Wat tried to comfort him. Jim's face felt hot. Wat pressed the poultice gently around the wound again and straightened the quilt. Gradually Jim stopped muttering and ceased to tremble so violently. From the way the fingers of his right hand were clenched into a hard knot, Wat could tell that he was fighting the pain.

After a while Jim murmured, "Hi, sprout! Where's Kit?" His voice was faint, but his words were clear. He looked at Wat and smiled weakly. He was himself again.

"Kit and Ma will be here soon," Wat said softly. Jim closed his eyes. Wat watched him until he fell asleep.

After Wat put more wood on the fire, he sat down in Ma's rocker again. He meant to stay awake, but the next sounds he heard were Kit and Ma talking—talking to Jim! Somehow he sensed that they must have been talking quite a while.

He jumped to his feet and blinked. The patient was wide-awake, but the doctor himself had fallen asleep!

Jim grinned at Wat. "Thanks, Doc, for the treatment," he said. "I feel pretty good now. In fact, I'm ready for something to eat. How about it, Ma?"

Wat Looks Ahead

It was soon after Jim came home wounded that the Reed family moved to Lawrenceville, Virginia. Now, in 1865, they were moving again. This time they went by train to Charlottesville, the home of the University of Virginia.

The long War between the States was over. The North and the South were once again the United States of America. The Virginians were poor, tired, hungry, and discouraged, but the Reverend Mr. Reed said the future was full of hope. The fighting was over.

He had just been appointed the Presiding Elder of the Charlottesville District. This meant that he would oversee all the churches and the preachers in that neighborhood.

Railway service had just started up again. The Reeds took the train in Blackstone instead of Lawrenceville. They were just settled in the wooden car when the engineer blew the whistle three times and they were off.

Wat and Kit settled in a seat across the aisle from their parents. They were excited because the train would stop at Farmville for dinner, and they would have a visit with Evan Macbeth and his family.

Wat leaned out the window. Black smoke came pouring from the large smokestack. The wind blew it his way. He pulled back quickly with a cinder in his eye and his face black with dirty smoke.

"Don't you look pretty for a young man of fourteen!" said Kit, with a laugh.

"Maybe, but I can prove that it's dirtier outside this car than inside." Wat grinned. "I wonder how soon we'll get to Farmville?"

"About noon, son," the conductor answered as he took their tickets. Wat frowned impatiently.

"It won't be much longer now until we see our Tom," Mrs. Reed said happily. "I hope he's doing well at the University."

"Jim's last letter was full of good news," Pa said. "I feel he will make a fine preacher."

"We'll miss our Lawrenceville friends," Ma said thoughtfully. "They took us in when they had little and divided happily with us. It was lovely living up on the top of that hill above the Meherrin River."

"Remember the day Wat and I were lost in the huckleberry swamp?" Kit said. "We were almost eaten alive by mosquitoes!"

"The neighbors didn't find us until after dark," Wat added. "You thought we'd get malaria afterward. Why was that, Pa?"

147

"I had heard that malaria was caused by a miasma, or damp air that hangs over a swamp at night," Pa explained. "Miasmas are supposed to bring on other kinds of fevers, too, even the dreadful yellow fever."

"Jim said that lots of the soldiers had that during the war," Kit said with a shudder. "It must be a terrible thing to have."

"The wounded suffered the most," Wat said at once. "I wonder why? Maybe it was because of their sores and——"

"Now that will do!" said Ma firmly. "No more war talk. It's time to look ahead to the fun you are going to have with Evan."

EVAN'S STORY

Mr. Macbeth was at the station to meet the Reeds. Everyone was excited. Everyone talked at once. Then Wat said, "Where's Evan?"

"In bed, poor lad," Mr. Macbeth said soberly. "He's having an attack of malaria, but he's growing better every day. He can hardly wait to see you boys. Run on ahead. Mother's waiting for you, too, just as eagerly as Evan."

Mrs. Macbeth was on the porch waving when Wat and Kit rounded the corner. She gave each one a big hug while she was saying how grown up they looked. Then she led them into the old sitting room, which was now Evan's bedroom.

Wat stopped at the door when he saw his old friend. Evan was lying half-propped up in bed against the pillows. His cheeks were sunken and pale. His face looked old. He held out a thin, white hand. Only his wide smile looked like the old Evan Wat had known.

"Hello!" he said in a weak but happy voice. "I thought you were never going to get here. How long can you stay?"

"Until the engineer of the train blows his

whistle three times," Wat said with a grin. "Say, I thought it was mostly soldiers who had malaria. You weren't in the army, were you?"

"No, but I was almost in a battle. Honest!" Evan answered, and his eyes seemed brighter.

"What do you mean?" Kit asked in surprise.

"Just what I said," Evan said quickly. "The last battle of the war was fought down by the river here."

"Our river?" Wat said in amazement. "Go on."

"First, prop me up a little more, Wat," Evan said slowly. "That's better. Well, you know General Lee's army had to—uh—leave Petersburg—uh—because they couldn't hold it. Then the Yankees followed them to Lynchburg."

"We know all that," Wat said impatiently.

"The Yanks caught up with some of our men at Sayler's Creek, about ten miles from here," Evan said. "It was an awful battle. Our boys had had little to eat and, besides, they had had forced

150

night marches for four days. They were all tired and hungry."

"They were brave, brave men," Kit said.

Evan's teeth began to chatter. "Wat, hand me that extra blanket," he said. It was a short while before he could go on. "The night of April 6, General Lee came into Farmville. He spent the night at Mrs. Logan's. You remember Mrs. Logan, don't you, Wat?"

"Sure, she made delicious cookies," Wat said. "Go on. What happened next?"

"Lots of people sent food to her house for the General's breakfast, but he had only a cup of tea," Evan said quietly. "I guess he wouldn't eat any more because his men had so little. Anyhow, he rode his gray horse, Traveler, to your old house to say a word of sympathy to Mrs. Thornton, who lives there now. Her husband was killed at the battle of Sharpsburg."

Evan's teeth were still chattering, but he went

on. "After that General Lee rode across the bridge to be sure the men who had escaped from Sayler's Creek had something to eat. General Breckenridge met him there. He was the Secretary of War, you know."

"We know," Kit said. "What next?"

"Then General Longstreet's men came marching right down Main Street," said Evan. "They were mighty grim and they were going fast, but the General stopped right in front of our house."

"Sure enough?" said Wat.

"Yes, and Ma asked him and his staff to have breakfast with us. Just then a messenger came galloping up. He told General Longstreet that Grant and his Yanks were right on his heels." Evan shivered and slipped under the covers.

"You mean none of our boys got anything to eat in Farmville?" Kit asked anxiously.

"Of course they did! The women cleaned out their pantries and smokehouses for them. Ma

152

had a whole baked ham and I carried it to the men myself," said Evan proudly.

"Was there any fighting right here in Farmville?" asked Wat, jumping to his feet. Evan nodded and took a long breath.

"There sure was!" he went on. "General Fitz Lee, General Robert Lee's nephew, was in command of our rear guard. His cavalry fought the Yank cavalry, hammer and tongs, at the edge of the town and right down the streets. That gave General Longstreet's men enough time to cross the bridge."

Just then Mrs. Macbeth came into the room with a tray of food, which she put down on the table beside Evan's bed.

"I thought you boys would rather eat in here with Evan than with us in the dining room," she said. "Don't talk too much, Evan. Let the boys tell you what they've been doing."

"Oh, I can't stop now," Evan said, sitting up

a little straighter. "I'm telling about the battle here in Farmville. They didn't know there was one."

"Oh, he just can't stop now!" cried Kit.

"Unless he should because of the malaria," said Wat, looking worried.

"Oh, I—feel—fine, Ma," said Evan. "Honest."

Mrs. Macbeth tucked him in carefully and gave him a dose of medicine. Evan made a face and Wat and Kit laughed.

"It's quinine, and it's bitter," Evan said.

"I think you boys do Evan more good than the medicine," Mrs. Macbeth said with a smile. "I don't think talking will do him any harm."

"Go on, now, if you can," said the boys after Mrs. Macbeth left the room. "Where were you when the fighting was going on?"

"You'll never guess." Evan grinned. "Orders were for all civilians to stay off the streets. I did. I was in the church tower. From there I could

154

see the sabers flashing and hear the carbines rattling. Believe me, it was exciting! The minute the last of Longstreet's men reached the bridge, Fitz Lee's troopers turned and went lickety-split down the street after them. They got to the bridge just in time."

"Where was Grant while all this was going on?" Kit asked.

"I'm coming to him," Evan said, sitting up straight again. Wat pushed him gently back.

"Take it easy," he said. "We'll eat while you get your breath. I think your Ma is worried."

"There's only a little left to tell," said Evan. "From then on everything seemed to happen at once. I guess Farmville was the busiest place in the whole world that day. When Grant rode into town you could tell he meant business. He went right to the hotel. Just as he got inside the door— *bang*, a cannonball hit the wall of the building. It's still there. You can see it."

"It was meant for Grant," said Wat quickly. "Did you see it hit?"

"I did. Well, pretty soon Grant came out on the porch of the hotel. He called an officer, gave him a paper, and the man went galloping down the street."

"I wonder what he wrote on the paper," Kit said. "Does anybody know?"

"Yes, it was the message asking General Lee to surrender," Evan replied.

"Never mind that part," said Wat quickly. "We know all about Appomattox and how wonderful General Lee was."

For a moment no one spoke. Evan closed his eyes. Wat pulled the covers up higher about Evan's shoulders and Kit stood looking out of the window.

"There, I'm fine now," Evan said in a little while. "My chill's over. That's why I'm not chattering any more. I'll get feverish pretty soon,

157

though. Then my head will hurt like thunder. I'll feel better tomorrow and the next day and then—bang—all over again."

"You mean you can tell what's going to happen next?" said Wat. "That's queer. Doesn't Doctor Ed know what to do? I thought he was such a good doctor."

"He's the best ever," said Evan. "Nobody knows as much as Doctor Ed."

"Well, I would hardly say that, my boy," said a hearty voice from the door. "How are you, boys?"

"Doctor Ed!" shouted Wat and Kit together.

"Need any leeches, sir?" Wat grinned. "Maybe they're just what Evan needs."

"Could be. I've tried everything else on my malarial patients," said Doctor Ed, half seriously. "As it is, I'm just thankful when I have enough quinine to keep them comfortable. It's up to some of you youngsters to find the cause and cure for all our fevers."

158

They talked a few minutes. Then the busy doctor hurried away, still chuckling over Wat's suggestion about the leeches.

"Wat, do you remember what I always said I was going to do when I grew up?" Evan said suddenly. "Open those shutters. I want to show you something. See that tobacco field? That's all mine."

"So you're going to be the biggest tobacco grower in the county," said Wat. "Good for you, Evan!"

"What about you fellows?" Evan asked. "What are you going to do?"

"I'm going to be a lawyer as soon as I finish the University," Kit said.

"I'm still not sure," Wat said slowly. "I have an idea for doing something right now, though, the three of us. Let's form a pact, and shake on it, that each time something important happens to one of us he writes to tell the other two about it. You know what I mean—say, when I do decide what I'm going to be."

"I'd like that fine," said Evan. "I hope important things happen to both of you soon. It's fun to get letters when you're sick."

They were shaking hands and grinning at each other when their families came into the room. Almost at once they heard three blasts from the engine whistle. They said good-by quickly. Wat began to run as soon as he was out-of-doors.

"I'm going to see that cannon ball," he called to his parents.

A few minutes later he came panting into the car and tumbled into his seat just as the train started to move.

"I saw it," Wat reported breathlessly. "All but one side is buried in the wall."

Wat was unusually quiet that afternoon. Finally Kit asked him what was wrong.

"I'm just thinking," he replied. "I don't see

160

why doctors or scientists don't learn all about malaria and other fevers. You know something? I might try myself!"

Kit grinned, but Pa and Ma looked interested. They all talked about the idea for a few minutes. Then the boys went back to their own thoughts as the train carried them north to Charlottesville and the University of Virginia.

Dr. Walter Reed

CHARLOTTESVILLE was in the foothills of the
Blue Ridge Mountains. Each year many families
came there to spend the summer. Wat wondered
why they did so.

He soon learned the answer. There were very
few cases of "the fever" in this clear mountain
air. In the low countries and along the seacoast
there were epidemics of malaria and even yellow
fever. Wat tucked this information in his mind
for future use.

"Maybe the place where people live has something to do with the diseases they have," he
thought as he trudged the long road home from

school. The school he attended was run by Mr. Abbot. He remembered that Evan could tell just what symptoms of his malaria would come next. This fact puzzled him.

"I'm going to Mr. Jefferson's university just as soon as I can," he said determinedly. "Maybe that's where I'll find the answers to some of my questions."

Virginians called the University of Virginia by this name. Thomas Jefferson, the third President of the United States, had designed the building and planned the University's first course of studies.

Wat admired Mr. Abbot, the headmaster of his school. For one thing, he had fought bravely for Virginia during the War between the States, but, even more important, his classes were interesting and exciting. Wat looked forward to the next two years.

He soon realized that it was hard for Pa to

keep four sons in private schools on his small salary. After thinking about this seriously, Wat made his first grown-up decision.

He went to Mr. Abbot and explained his problem. He asked for permission to take two years of work in one. The headmaster listened and thought the matter over. Finally he granted Wat's request.

"I'll keep it a secret from everyone but Kit, Evan, and Mr. Abbot," Wat decided. "Pa and Ma will worry if I study so hard. I'll write my first pact letter to Evan while he's still sick."

Wat finished the year's work with honors. Pa and Ma were very proud of him, but Ma said she was going to hide his books all summer and "feed him up proper."

This was one of the few vacations in which Wat had a really good time. He and his friends took long walks, had picnics, and talked, talked, and talked. Fall came all too soon, and Wat became one of the four hundred students at the University of Virginia.

First-year students at the University took the same subjects: languages, history, mathematics, and sciences. Wat enjoyed the science classes most, but he soon grew restless. He was chiefly interested in laboratory experiments, but most of the lessons were from books.

He soon decided that he wanted to graduate in one year instead of two so that he could get "out in the world." The only way he could do this, he learned, was to study medicine.

He liked the idea of becoming a doctor, for ever since Evan's illness he had been interested in the study of medicine. However, to finish the medical course in one year, he had to have special permission from the Board of Professors.

The board was made up of Wat's own professors and four others whom he did not know. On the morning of his appointment, Wat stood before these men with his head up and his blue eyes shining. He answered the professors' questions carefully, then waited quietly for their decision.

Finally the chairman of the Board said, "Mr. Reed, it would be unwise for a boy of seventeen to become a doctor."

"If I can pass the medical examinations next June do you think that my age should count against me, sir?" Wat asked quietly. "I would appreciate a chance to prove myself."

The professors walked to the end of the room, where Wat could not hear them.

Wat's mouth was dry. The palms of his hands were moist. He was excited but not frightened.

At last the professors returned to the table, and Wat straightened his shoulders. The chairman cleared his throat.

"Mr. Reed, we have decided to grant your request," he said seriously. "You will receive your medical degree in June if you pass your examinations." Wat took a long breath and stepped forward.

"Thank you, gentlemen," he said. "I shall hold you to your promise."

That year Wat often studied until after midnight and was up again with the sun.

"All work and no play make Jack a dull boy," Pa often told him. "Besides, you will ruin your health, son." Wat nodded in agreement but continued to study.

Finally examination days came. Wat was ready for them. He passed easily and finished third highest in his class. He was the youngest man in the history of the University of Virginia to pass the medical examinations after one year's preparation. Dr. Walter Reed was only seventeen years old.

That evening was a wonderful one for the Reed family. Ma made her famous apple pie for supper. Pa thanked God for all his past blessings and asked His help, for all his boys, in the years ahead of them.

Wat wrote Evan his second important letter. He told him that the next morning he and Kit, doctor and lawyer, would go to New York City to seek their fortunes.

THE HUNT IS ON

Young Dr. Reed went on duty at the Bellevue Hospital Medical College on the morning after he and Kit arrived in New York City. His first assignment was to take notes as he followed the older doctors from patient to patient.

He had read about typhoid fever, smallpox, and diphtheria, but he had never seen their terrible effects on men, women, and children. Many times during this hot summer he asked several doctors the same question: "How are these diseases spread from one person to another?"

168

"Young man, it's our duty to try to cure our patients," they all told him. "Just keep your mind on that."

Wat shook his head and set his jaw. Such an answer did not satisfy him.

He spent many of his leisure hours in the library, studying such diseases as typhoid fever and malaria. Malaria was now thought by some doctors to be spread by mosquitoes. This was an exciting idea to Wat.

Wat spent much time in the slums, from which many of his patients came. He was disgusted by the filth, poverty, and disease that he found in the ramshackle buildings where most foreign-born immigrants lived.

"Flies! flies! flies!" he thought as he brushed them off the face of a sick baby. "Dirty insects!" That evening as he was studying, he suddenly jumped to his feet and whistled.

"If mosquitoes carry malaria, why can't flies

169

spread typhoid?" he thought. He walked up and down the room with quick steps. Dr. Walter Reed was "on the hunt" to find answers to his own questions.

The children of the slums loved young Dr. Reed. Their parents liked him, too, but some of them thought he was too young.

"I'm going to grow a nice, long, bushy beard," Wat said to Kit one evening.

"You'd better add a long-tailed coat and glasses," Kit said with a laugh.

After two years in New York, Dr. Reed received his second medical degree. This time it was from Bellevue. Now he was asked to practice in other hospitals, too.

When Wat was twenty-one he was appointed District Physician in the slum area. At twenty-two he was made one of five Health Inspectors for Brooklyn.

One of his duties in this job was to see that

buildings, vacant lots, streets, and even homes were cleaned up. He insisted that people keep things clean.

"If I could only prove what I think about flies!" he thought sadly one day as he was filling out another death certificate. "If we don't clean these places up and get rid of the flies, we'll have a typhoid epidemic. I wish I had time to really work on the problem."

After he had been in New York five years, Wat could have had a good, well-paid private practice, but his heart was not in it. He was more interested in trying to track down the cause of typhoid fever.

Suddenly he grew tired of crowds, bad smells, dirt, flies, and even himself. He thought he ought to be doing better.

"Take a week's vacation," Kit advised. "Go home and fish and walk and talk with Pa."

Wat did. While he was home he met a young

lady named Emilie Lawrence. Wat knew almost at once that he wanted to marry her. However, he also knew that before he could he must have a regular salary.

Neither he nor Emilie wanted to live in a city. Finally Wat took the examinations for the Medical Corps of the United States Army and became a medical officer. Then at last he and Emilie were married.

At the age of twenty-four, First Lieutenant Walter Reed and his wife were sent to his first post at Fort Lowell, Arizona.

For the next fifteen years Lieutenant, and soon Captain, Walter Reed was transferred from one fort to another in Arizona, Nebraska, Dakota, and other out-of-the-way places. His son and daughter were born in the West.

Captain Reed was responsible for the health not only of the soldiers and their families, but of the Indians and settlers as well. He often

thought of his "circuit riding" pa as he himself rode miles and miles, day and night, to answer sick calls.

During these years Wat had little time for anything but the care of his patients. He did not realize that because of his intelligent work in out-of-the-way places, he was building a strong foundation for his future work.

He became skillful at recognizing diseases, and was forced to make his own decisions. Each detail of what he did was as perfect as possible.

Once in a while friends sent him medical pamphlets. He pored over these as carefully as he used to study his books. It was from one of these pamphlets that he learned that the fly *was* a typhoid carrier. He smiled as he remembered that in New York he had thought that this might be true.

He began to long more and more for a chance to study again. Finally, in 1890 he asked for, and was granted, a post in Baltimore, Maryland, the home of Johns Hopkins University. Now he could find time to work in the laboratory of the famous scientist and teacher, Dr. William Welch.

Wat's particular interest was pathology, the science of treating disease, and bacteriology, the study of microbes or germs.

The next eight years were full of rewarding work for Wat. By the time of the Spanish-American War, he was an authority on typhoid fever and several other diseases.

After the war, Wat, who was now a major, was appointed chairman of a group of doctors whose task was to wipe out typhoid fever in southern army camps. Before he had finished this job, he was appointed head of still another group of doctors and scientists and sent to Cuba.

Yellow fever was raging in Cuba, and the task of Wat and the doctors on this new commission

175

was to find the cause of yellow fever and some way to prevent it.

One day late in June of 1900, Major Walter Reed and his friend Dr. James Carroll stood at the railing of a small ship as it entered the harbor at Havana, Cuba. Walter Reed squared his shoulders and silently prayed for God's help. The great work of his life was about to begin.

The Kill

ONE DAY in 1901 young Johnny Macbeth rushed into his grandfather's sitting room in Farmville, Virginia. His grandfather was Evan Macbeth, Walter Reed's boyhood friend.

"Grandpa! Grandpa!" Johnny cried excitedly. "Here's a letter from Cuba. I'll bet it's from Major Reed." Johnny had met Major Reed two years before when the latter was visiting Farmville. Ever since, he had been greatly interested in the Major's work.

"Suppose you get another log for the fireplace while I read the letter," his grandfather said with a smile.

177

Johnny hurried outdoors. When he returned, he put the log on the fire and settled himself to listen. "The last letter you had said he was being sent to Cuba to study—was it yellow fever?" he said.

"That's right," replied his grandfather. "This letter tells how he and another doctor, named Carroll, were met in Cuba by Dr. Lazear and Dr. Agramonte, the two other members of the commission. Major Reed had not met them before."

"What happened?" asked Johnny.

"Well, the four doctors went almost at once to the army hospital," Mr. Macbeth said. "There they saw bed after bed, each holding a yellow fever patient. Dr. Agramonte told the others that yellow fever had killed more American soldiers during the war with Spain than Spanish soldiers had.

"Then he went on to explain that yellow fever

played strange tricks. It might strike one man in one tent and all but one man in the next. This seemed very strange.

"Of course, the commission already knew that if a person once has yellow fever and lives, he won't have it again. They also knew that yellow fever epidemics start in the lowlands in hot summer weather, usually near water. However, these were all the known facts.

"Dr. Agramonte was the only one in the group who had had yellow fever, so he was the only one who was really safe. The others knew that they were in danger of catching yellow fever, but they did not worry about it."

"They were really brave men," Johnny interrupted him.

"Yes, they were," his grandfather went on. "The first thing Major Reed did after seeing the hospital was to hold a meeting with the other three doctors to discuss plans. Before they could do anything else, they had to decide what to look for, where to look, and how to look for it.

"First of all, they discussed the possibility that yellow fever was contagious. A contagious disease is one which you can catch by coming in contact with someone who has it. Many people believed that yellow fever *was* contagious. They kept patients away from well people and burned everything that belonged to them, even their bedding and furniture."

"Did that keep the fever from spreading?" asked Johnny curiously.

"No, it still struck without warning," his grandfather replied. "Then Dr. Lazear told about an experience he had had during an epidemic in a village called Quemados. Many people came down with the fever there, but none of the nurses who cared for them caught it."

"What did that mean?" Johnny asked.

"Well, it seemed to prove that yellow fever

was not contagious," his grandfather continued. "However, this had not actually been proved, so Major Reed and the other doctors decided to drop the idea for the time being.

"Next Major Reed wondered whether yellow fever might be carried by some insect or animal. It had already been learned that mosquitoes carried malaria. Was it possible that they carried yellow fever, too?

" 'There is a doctor named Carlos Finlay here in Havana who thinks they do,' Dr. Agramonte told the men.

" 'We'll go to see him in the morning,' Major Reed decided, and with that the four men separated for the night.

"Dr. Finlay was glad to talk to the four doctors. He told them about his experiments. 'Since 1881, I have been convinced that mosquitoes carry yellow fever,' he said, 'but I have been unable to prove it.'

"He gave Major Reed and the others some of the mosquitoes he had raised. The doctors took the mosquitoes back to their laboratory. There they carried out more careful experiments than Dr. Finlay had been able to make. What they learned seemed to prove that mosquitoes might actually be the villains. However, the doctors could not prove that this was true."

"Why not?" Johnny asked.

"Well, most medical experiments are carried out on animals," said his grandfather. "Major Reed and his associates soon discovered that animals can't catch yellow fever. As a result, the Major had to make a very difficult decision."

"What kind of decision?"

"He had to decide whether to try and give yellow fever to human beings."

"Goodness!" Johnny's eyes grew wide. "Wouldn't that be dangerous?"

"Very dangerous, because it might cause death," his grandfather replied. "For this reason, the doctors decided to experiment only on themselves at first. Before they could start, however, Major Reed was called back to Washington for a conference on typhoid fever."

"He wouldn't leave his men at a time like that!" Johnny exclaimed confidently.

"He had no choice," said his grandfather. "A

good soldier obeys orders. The Major left at once. He hoped to return before the experiment began, but he told the others to go ahead without him if he didn't."

"Weren't they afraid?" asked Johnny.

"They may have been, but they were soldiers fighting a dreadful enemy," said Mr. Macbeth. "They knew that one life, or more, given to learn how to prevent yellow fever might save thousands of lives later. Like all good soldiers, they were willing to risk death.

"First Dr. Lazear hatched some mosquito eggs. When the mosquitoes were full grown, he let them bite some yellow fever victims. This made the mosquitoes carriers of yellow fever."

"What do you mean?" asked Johnny.

"When a mosquito bites a person, it takes some of his blood. Major Reed and his associates knew that the mysterious thing that caused yellow fever was hidden in the patient's blood. They knew it wasn't a bacterium—a germ that could be seen—because they couldn't find it. Therefore, it had to be smaller than the very smallest bacterium.

"When all this was done, the doctors were ready to start their experiment. Dr. Lazear was the first to let himself be bitten. It must have been a serious moment when he held out his arm to that mosquito."

Mr. Macbeth paused, and Johnny said excitedly, "Go on, Grandpa! Don't stop now. What happened next? Did Major Reed and Dr. Lazear learn anything?"

Mr. Macbeth glanced at Major Reed's letter again. "Well, Dr. Lazear didn't get yellow fever. Next Dr. Carroll let himself be bitten by a mosquito that had bitten four sick men. He got the fever and almost died. Then Dr. Lazear let himself be bitten again. Within a few days he contracted yellow fever and died."

"Oh!" There was a moment of silence. "How *awful!*" Then Johnny added, "Was that enough just to prove that mosquitoes were the carriers, though, Grandpa?"

"No," his grandfather answered. "Major Reed and the others redoubled their efforts in order to be sure. First of all, they built several small cabins in which to carry on further tests. The cabins were screened so that mosquitoes could not get in or out. The doctors named these cabins 'Camp Lazear.' Then they asked for volunteers who were willing to let infected mosquitoes bite them.

"Two men, Privates John R. Kessinger and John J. Moran, came forward at once. They refused to take money. They wanted to help for humanity's sake, they said. Other men volunteered, too. They all came down with yellow fever, but, fortunately, no one died.

"In the first test, Major Reed wanted to prove

that yellow fever could be spread only by mosquitoes. He wanted to be sure that it was not contagious, too."

"How did he do that?" asked Johnny.

"Three soldiers who had been kept in one of the cabins for some time, away from mosquitoes, spent several days and nights in another cabin. Here they used the same soiled nightshirts, sheets, and beds that yellow fever patients had used. The men could not even go out into the fresh air to eat. Yet not one of them got yellow fever."

"Surely that proved that yellow fever wasn't contagious!" Johnny said.

"Maybe so, but Major Reed still wasn't satisfied. He kept on with his tests until he determined that only one species or kind of mosquito carried yellow fever. Not only that, he discovered that only the female of that species was a yellow fever carrier."

"So that was why Dr. Lazear didn't get fever the first time he was bitten!" Johnny said. "The mosquitoes weren't the right kind."

"That was part of it," said his grandfather. "The other part was the timing. Major Reed and his associates also discovered that to carry infected blood, a mosquito had to bite a patient during the first three days he had yellow fever. Then at least twelve days had to pass before the mosquito could infect anyone else."

"Did the Major ever find what caused yellow fever?" Johnny asked.

"Yes, it was a particle too tiny to be seen through a microscope. Such a particle, which often is alive, is called a filterable virus. It is so tiny that it goes through the finest filters or strainers that doctors use in their laboratories."

"What will Major Reed do now that his job in Cuba is finished?" Johnny wondered.

"His job isn't finished yet," said Mr. Macbeth.

"He still has to keep yellow fever from spreading. However, he has already suggested how that can be done."

"How?"

"Mosquitoes lay their eggs in low places where water stands," his grandfather explained. "If such places are cleaned out and drained, the mosquito eggs can't hatch. That alone will help to wipe out yellow fever. Then, too, people can screen their houses to keep out the mosquitoes that do breed. If people do this everywhere, yellow fever will soon be under control."

Johnny was silent for several moments, thinking. Then he looked at his grandfather and said proudly, "I'll bet Major Reed is one of the best doctors in the whole world, don't you?"

"He's a fine doctor, certainly," his grandfather replied. "He doesn't give up until he knows the truth about a disease. He was like that when we were boys. He always wanted to know."

190

Major Walter Reed died on November 17, 1902, and was buried in Arlington National Cemetery outside Washington, D.C. Cut in his tombstone are the words: "He gave to man the control over that dread scourge, Yellow Fever."

Even before Major Reed's death, Colonel William Crawford Gorgas, the American sanitation officer in Cuba, had drained stagnant pools and ditches and rid Cuba of yellow fever.

Two years later Colonel Gorgas went to the Panama Canal Zone. There, too, following Walter Reed's suggestions, he succeeded in controlling the mosquito that carried yellow fever and made the Canal Zone safe for the men who were digging the Panama Canal. Thus, Walter Reed, who died before our country started to work on the Canal, helped to make it possible.

A grateful country has not forgotten Walter Reed. The great army medical center in the city of Washington, D.C., is known as the Walter Reed Memorial Hospital. In Belroi, Virginia, the little house in which Walter Reed was born is now a museum. At the top of the Army Register's Roll of Honor, listing the men who worked to wipe out yellow fever, is the name of Walter Reed, the young man who wanted to know.

WHEN WALTER REED LIVED

1851   WALTER REED WAS BORN IN BELROI, VIRGINIA, SEPTEMBER 13.

There were 31 states in the Union.

Millard Fillmore was President.

The population of the country was about 24,016,000.

1858–
1862   WALTER ATTENDED PIEDMONT ACADEMY IN LIBERTY, VIRGINIA.

Abraham Lincoln was President of the Union, 1861-1865.

Jefferson Davis was President of the Confederacy, 1861-1865.

The first transcontinental telegraph was completed, 1861.

The War between the States was fought, 1861-1865.

1865   WALTER MOVED WITH HIS FAMILY TO CHARLOTTESVILLE, VIRGINIA.

Abraham Lincoln was assassinated, April 14, 1865.

Andrew Johnson was President, 1865-1869.

Thirteenth Amendment to the Constitution, forbidding slavery, was ratified, 1865.

1867–
1870

WALTER STUDIED MEDICINE AT THE UNIVERSITY OF VIRGINIA AND BELLEVUE HOSPITAL.

The United States purchased Alaska, 1867.

The first transcontinental railroad was completed, 1869.

Ulysses S. Grant was President, 1869-1877.

1875

LT. WALTER REED WAS ASSIGNED TO HIS FIRST POST AT FORT LOWELL, ARIZONA.

Alexander Graham Bell invented the telephone, 1876.

Rutherford B. Hayes was President, 1877-1881.

Thomas A. Edison invented the phonograph, 1878, and the electric light, 1879.

Clara Barton founded the American Red Cross, 1881.

1890

DR. WALTER REED WORKED IN THE LABORATORY OF DR. WILLIAM WELCH IN BALTIMORE.

Henry Ford built his first automobile, 1896.

William B. McKinley was President, 1897-1901.

Spanish-American War was fought, 1898.

1900   MAJOR WALTER REED WAS DIRECTOR OF COM-
MISSION TO FIND CAUSE OF YELLOW FEVER.

U. S. Army Dental Corps and U. S. Army Nurse Corps were organized, 1901.

President McKinley was assassinated, 1901.

1902   MAJOR WALTER REED DIED IN NOVEMBER.

There were 45 states in the Union.

Theodore Roosevelt was President.

The population of the country was about 76,313,000.

DO YOU REMEMBER?

1. Why did the Reed family move so often?
2. Why did Walter like to move?
3. Why did Bessie Sue save the catfish whiskers for Wat?
4. How did Evan suggest earning money for a new fishing pole?
5. What plant did Wat and Evan use to make medicine to heal mosquito bites?
6. What did the letters S. H. P. stand for?
7. What did Mr. Payne mean by the "Big Wheel"?

195

8. What did Mr. Reed always do before moving from a parsonage?

9. How many birthday cakes were there for Wat at the farewell picnic?

10. Whose home was at Poplar Forest, and whose home was at Monticello?

11. What were "credit words" at Piedmont Academy?

12. What was the title of Wat's winning paper at Piedmont Academy?

13. Where did General Grant write his note asking General Lee to surrender?

14. What happened to Walter when he was seventeen?

15. What was Walter doing when he was twenty-one?

16. What insect carries malaria?

17. What insect carries typhoid fever?

18. Where is Walter Reed buried?

19. Where is the Walter Reed Memorial Hospital?

IT'S FUN TO LOOK UP THESE THINGS

1. Where does bamboo grow and what are some of its uses?

2. How were leeches used to treat sick people when Wat was a boy?

3. What are the Peaks of Otter and where are they located?

4. In what town did the War between the States end?

5. What is a ciphering race?

6. What is the difference between a dictionary and an encyclopedia?

7. What is a hurricane lamp?

8. In what parts of the world do people still have malaria?

INTERESTING THINGS YOU CAN DO

1. Draw a map of Virginia and locate the towns in which Wat and his family lived at different times during his life.

2. Draw a picture of an ox cart and one of a three-seated carriage such as the one Wat and his family used to go to Liberty.

3. Find pictures of the University of Virginia at Charlottesville and of Monticello, Thomas Jefferson's home near by.

4. Look at a mosquito and other insects through a strong magnifying glass or, if possible, a microscope. Try to draw a picture of what you see.
5. Find pictures of different kinds of insects, label them, and make a display on the bulletin board.

OTHER BOOKS YOU MAY ENJOY READING

Doctors Who Conquered Yellow Fever, Ralph Nading Hill. Trade Edition, Random House. School Edition, Hale.

George Carver: Boy Scientist, Augusta Stevenson. Trade and School Editions, Bobbs-Merrill.

Pasteur and the Invisible Giant, Edward Dolan. Dodd.

They Wanted the Real Answers, Amabel Williams-Ellis. Putnam.

Will and Charlie Mayo: Doctor's Boys, Marie Hammontree. Trade and School Editions, Bobbs-Merrill.

INTERESTING WORDS IN THIS BOOK

accurate (ăk′ů rĭt) : exact, true

ague (ā′gū) : malarial fever which causes a person to feel hot, then cold and shaking

associate ($\breve{a}$ sō'shĭ āt) : friend, partner, comrade

bacteriology (băk tēr'ĭ ŏl'ô jĭ) : science dealing with bacteria

bacterium (băk tēr'ĭ $\breve{u}$m) : germ large enough to be seen under a microscope

bloodletting: bleeding a sick person by cutting or by using a leech

boughten (bôt''n) : purchased, not homemade

cipher (sī'fẽr) : do sums in arithmetic

commendation (kŏm'ĕn dā'shŭn) : praise, approval

complicated (kŏm'plĭ kāt'ĕd) : involved, made up of many parts

determined (dė tûr'mĭnd) : having one's mind made up, resolute

difference (dĭf'ẽr ĕns) : disagreement

epidemic (ĕp'ĭ dĕm'ĭk) : disease affecting many persons in a community

filterable (fĭl'tẽr $\dot{a}$ b'l) : capable of being strained or filtered

hammer and tongs: with all one's strength and energy

interrupt (ĭn'tĕ rŭpt') : to break into a conversation or action

laboratory (lăb′ȯ rȧ tō′rĭ) : place for scientific study and experiments

magnify (măg′nĭ fī) : enlarge, make larger

miasma (mī ăz′mȧ) : poisonous vapor or atmosphere

mountaineer: person who lives in the mountains

mysterious (mĭs tēr′ĭ ŭs) : hidden, hard to understand or explain

nourishment (nûr′ĭsh mĕnt) : food

Orient (ō′rĭ ĕnt) : countries of Asia generally

pathology (pȧ thŏl′ȯ jĭ) : science of treating diseases and their causes

pennyroyal: sweet-smelling plant of the mint family

regretful (rḗ grĕt′fo͞ol) : sorry

sassafras (săs′ȧ frăs) : tree or shrub whose dried leaves and roots are used as a medicine

scientific (sī′ĕn tĭf′ĭk) : pertaining to or used in science

scourge (skûrj) : great calamity or trouble, as severe illness; punishment

stock: close-fitting wide necktie

taunt: tease or insult

thorough (thû′rȯ) : exact, careful about details

wry: twisted

200